THE IRISH TIMES

HEART

MAURICE NELIGAN

BEAT

D1225806

Edited by: Deirdre Veldon

Published by: The Irish Times Limited
Edited by: Deirdre Veldon
Design & Layout: Kevin O'Hare
Colour reproduction: Irish Times Premedia

ISBN 978-0-907011-36-1

Foreword

Maurice Neligan was already a household name in Ireland by the time he started to write a weekly column for The Irish Times Health Supplement in early 2004. He had enjoyed a distinguished career as a pioneering heart surgeon, who carried out more than 15,000 operations over five decades. In 1975, he performed the first coronary bypass graft at Dublin's Mater hospital, and in 1985 led the team that carried out the Republic's first heart transplant operation. He also pioneered the development of open heart surgery in children.

Born in 1937, Maurice grew up in Booterstown, Co Dublin and never strayed far. He attended Blackrock College and went on to study medicine at University College Dublin. After his graduation in 1962, he went to work at the Mater hospital and he became a core member of the team at the national cardiac surgical centre in the hospital in 1971.

His retirement in 2002 left him with time and enthusiasm, which he initially tried to deploy around his home, to the consternation of his family, as he later wrote. Thus, he was dispatched to accept the offer to write a column for The Irish Times. And so, with some reluctance, he taught himself how to use a computer and became a part-time journalist.

When as founding editor of the Health Supplement, I asked him to contribute a column, his main concern was that he might not have enough to say on such a frequent basis. After his first column, the issue never arose again. Notwithstanding his great willingness to stir debate, he always displayed his inherent wisdom when on a rare occasion it was quietly suggested that another word might be more tempered than the one he had chosen.

From the beginning, Maurice realised the freedom to write and express one's views was an opportunity not afforded to many and he treated this responsibility with respect. He was direct and fearless in his criticism of the health service, notably those who were responsible for it politically. His passion and sense of justice were palpable when he was writing about the inequities created by government health policy.

He attracted controversy for his forthright views on the health service, but he was at his best when writing about the things he held dearest; Kerry, his medical education and his beloved family.

Maurice's wife, Pat, achieved a little celebrity in her own right as the Highest Authority alluded to regularly in the column. She was the target of much fond humour from her husband, who liked to characterise himself as a mere hapless male in her formidable presence. He was immensely proud of his seven children.

Maurice Neligan passed away suddenly at the age of 73, leaving a void in the lives of his family and numerous friends and the many readers of his column in The Irish Times. He is deeply missed.

Kevin O'Sullivan,
Editor, The Irish Times
October 2011

Maurice Christopher Neligan: born May 15th, 1937; died October 8th, 2010

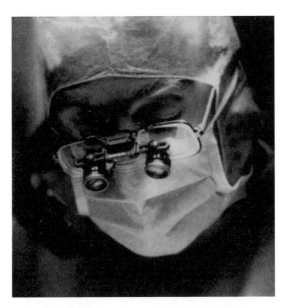

HEALTH SERVICE

Beware of health police

It was with no little astonishment that I recently heard a colleague state on steam radio that we Irish had a great record of compliance with the law. It just goes to show how wrong I can be as I would have supposed the opposite to be true. Mind you he was talking about the smoking ban which has made us all healthier and emptied the hospitals.

Dare I ask why the patients still lie in undiminished, even increasing numbers on trolleys? We were told that the effects on respiratory conditions and on heart attacks would be immediate. The decline in the various cancers attributed to smoking would understandably take more time. I reiterate my simple query. Why are the patients still on trolleys in considerable numbers? Have they not read that they are supposed to be healthier, with less chest conditions and heart attacks? Couldn't they be like all the newly healthy barmen who no longer clog the A&E departments? Have they no shame?

Incidentally the trolleys numbers game poses an interesting conundrum. There appears to be a divergence of opinion as to how many patients enjoy this privilege on a daily basis. The Irish Nurses Organisation gives one figure (the higher). The administrators proffer another (the lower). Whom should one believe? All the nurses I knew could count. Maybe this ability is no longer required as part of their new training courses. In any case, what possible benefit accrues to the nurse in exaggerating the true and awful situation? I can clearly see a benefit on the other side of the equation as concealment of the true state of the health services has become an art form over the years.

The answer to this question is obvious. Let these unfortunate patients be counted at an agreed time by representatives of the doctors, nurses and administrators. The agreed figures throughout the country and their regional variations could then be made available, not only to the powers that be, but also made known publicly. We can then see improvement happening as we have been promised. Doctors and nurses must retain their obligations as patient advocates. Concealment of the true state of affairs is in the interest of nobody.

In this context, a young consultant doctor, recently appointed, found that no facilities existed for the position in question, no space, no staff, and no beds. Local approaches having proved fruitless, he spoke publicly about this farcical situation. The doctor was summoned to meet the administration, not, it was stressed, for a disciplinary hearing, just a general warning about the creation of waves.

I and many of my colleagues throughout the country who have spoken out about the conditions of the service are familiar with this marine phenomenon. If you little doctor fish make waves, we administrator fish can make bigger ones, even tsunami if you annoy us sufficiently.

Co-operation between all branches of the caring professions and administration remains the only way forward. The latter should strive to make the doctors and nurses' tasks easier, and should themselves, without fear, highlight deficiencies. There are many excellent and dedicated administrators, and one can understand some reluctance to put jobs and promotional prospects in jeopardy by speaking contrary to the official line. We need an open atmosphere where problems of whatever nature can be aired and not hidden.

In the meantime, having abolished smoking and drinking in our fantasy land, we must establish another fear. Apparently this time it is going to be obesity. We

9

can expect the usual outpourings and calls for repentance and salvation before this cataclysm of fat envelops us all and costs the State millions in extra health costs. Considering that the State cannot provide a service right now, this should prove interesting. I have already made this simple observation before and I will make it again.

We will not save any money for the State by preventing people dying from excesses of tobacco, alcohol, obesity or anything else. The world is still ordered such that everyone dies and the ultimate cause of death is not necessarily less expensive than that prevented by adhering to the good life as deemed by some. We doctors should be stressing the benefits of moderation, the wellbeing that ensues and the chances of extending useful and pleasurable life. We should not preach that whatever our particular crusade may be, it will somehow save the State money. It will not.

I do not wish to write about such subjects for the rest of my days. Would it be possible to instil some common sense into these endless debates? We all know the problems of excess. We can provide education in these matters but we must accept also that individuals have free will. Some individuals become addicted to things that are bad for them. As doctors we must treat with compassion, and as best we can. Moderation in all things including moderation itself should be the goal. We must live alongside each other and tolerate our respective frailties.

Do we really need smoke police, drink police, fat police? I think not and they certainly won't save us any money. I am afraid the obesity scare is upon us now and won't depart anytime soon. More about this anon, in the constant fight to stop the lunatics possessing the asylum. In the meantime, enjoy what may be your last Mars bar.

April 5th, 2005

The next crisis on the menu

In this mountain shall the Lord of Hosts, make unto all the people a feast of fat things, a feast of wine on the lees, of fat things full of marrow.
(Isaiah 25:6)

Pretty irresponsible of God I would have thought, he must have known that an epidemic of obesity was coming down the line. Perhaps he forgot or had things of more importance on his mind. He obviously hadn't read the report of the taskforce on obesity, because they clearly outline the crisis ahead. More publicity, more spin, dire predictions of Biblical intensity about the ultimate fate of the populace, I wonder that we survive at all.

At the risk of being a bore might I point out that we have survived the millennium bug, and thus far nuclear immolation, and even passive smoking. We have endured many other crises, some real, most imaginary, and we are still here, with increasing prosperity and, dare I say it, increased longevity.

However, we must have a fear from which Big Brother (the nanny state) can protect us. Does it occur to these people that given our education we ought to be able to protect ourselves and our children? We are told that obesity costs us €500 million per year. How on earth would anybody know that? Think of a figure, double it, and then run with it to fan the flames of the latest official fear. We are thankfully in a time of prosperity and suffering from some of the diseases of affluence rather than poverty. Whether we are getting a little fatter would seem to be of little import in the general scheme of things.

Education and common sense tell us that we should eat moderately and take exercise. We know these simple precepts but sadly many do not adhere to them. Ironically those who do seem in the long run to do little better than their less meticulous brethren. I would contend that other than through education, the State should have little part to play in the lifestyle choices of the individual, provided such are not anti-social and injurious to the common good.

I fear another quango to dictate our food choices. More public servants pushing paper at each other and saying what the Minister wants, while the working, producing citizens see their rights eroded a little further. We have the pompously named Office of Tobacco Control. What would we name this one? The Office for Vegetable Promotion? No, that sounds too much like the Department of Health itself. We need a new and striking name that will rivet attention and point out that we are digging our graves with our teeth. I invite suggestions as to an appropriate name.

God be with the time when we were told that "an apple a day keeps the doctor away". Now we are enjoined to have at least five fruit or vegetable servings a day to ward off illness and to vaguely hint at immortality. Perhaps the populace should be issued with a clove of garlic and a pointed stake to ward off vampires, medical or otherwise. Let us not forget the iodine tablets. The report, I am led to believe, recommends a sort of Kristallnacht on the vending machines in primary schools. Apparently there are hardly any. So much for the research!

Jack and Jill
Went up the hill
To fetch a pail of water
Jack fell down

And broke his crown
And Jill came tumbling after.

There is another side to this equation. It is freely acknowledged by all that we are not getting enough exercise. The Taoiseach says he is shocked to hear of the insurance problems encountered by schools. What planet does he live on? Certainly not this one, but I guess we knew that already. In the modern era Jack wouldn't have gone near the hill as his mother would probably have driven. If he had walked, why did he fall? Was there a pothole and if on a farm, was the farmer insured? If within the school grounds, was he properly supervised? Was he forbidden to run? Was post-traumatic stress counselling available for Jill? We know our rights now.

Can Government do something useful about the culture of litigation for compensation within this State? Schools, playgrounds and sports facilities (where they exist) are paralysed by increasing insurance costs, partly reflecting spiralling claims. School trips, field trips, adventure holidays and activities organised by voluntary groups are disappearing under threat of litigation on various fronts. This culture, preventing or curtailing normal exercise patterns, is a far greater threat to the wellbeing of our children than a few bars of chocolate or bags of crisps.

If it makes you feel better, get rid of the vending machines in these schools. While you are at it, you might as well fix the heating and mend the holes in the roof. Adequate hygienic toilets could be provided and the rats could be chased away. You could provide proper playgrounds and sports facilities in general. Above all, you could tackle the creeping strangulation of opportunistic litigation.

Up Jack got
And home did trot
As fast as he could caper
To old Dame Dob
Who patched his nob
With vinegar and brown paper.

Even at that tender age he knew enough to stay away from the local A&E department.

May 24th, 2005

13

Signing up for defensive medicine

Primum non nocere

First do no harm has been a guiding principle of medical management since pre-Hippocratic days. Few doctors get up in the morning and say "I'm going to harm somebody today." Yet it happens and will continue to happen as long as mankind is divided into the two categories of doctor and patient.

I have had recent conversations with two patients with widely different conditions, attending two different consultants for their treatment. In both instances, the clinicians had not alone discussed in detail, the diagnosis, prognosis and treatment of their conditions, but had provided a written synopsis of same.

In other words, the doctor was trying to obtain "informed consent" for the proposed course of treatment. What baffled both patients - intelligent and successful in their own fields - was that despite what appeared to me to be lucid explanations of the problems, it was almost incomprehensible to them.

As an intern, getting consent forms signed was part of daily life and by and large the patients accepted the proposed treatment in trust and with good faith.

What has changed of course over the years is the increasingly oppressive climate of litigation. Who can I sue if things go wrong? It must be somebody's fault. They never told me this could happen. Accordingly, now the doctor must explain the nature and extent of proposed treatments and their likely outcomes. He is supposed to list any complications that may arise up to and including death. He is supposed to inform patients of alternative treatments and their purported efficacy. In the US, this must include the likely costs involved.

All of this ignores one basic problem - the patient, in the absence of a medical degree, does not have the knowledge to engage meaningfully with the doctor. Many doctors entrusting themselves to their specialist brethren do not understand the intricacies and problems known to the specialist. But they do have the knowledge and sense to trust.

So how far is the profession to go in establishing informed consent? One little example: the California supreme court on the risks of having blood drawn listed haematoma, dermatitis, cellulitis, abscess, osteomyelitis, septicaemia, endocarditis, thrombophlebitis, pulmonary embolism and death. It stressed that the list was by no means complete. Another publication listing complications of back surgery listed 146 complications with the same caveat as before. So how far do we go?

Does the doctor list every known complication of the procedure or just those more likely to occur? If, by listing every known hazard, he scares the patient so completely that the treatment is declined, he may be deemed negligent for so doing. If he omits complications and sequelae which might seem obvious, he can also be deemed negligent.

If the doctor makes a judgment call that the patient is incapable of grasping the intricacies of what is proposed, he becomes totally politically incorrect, and indeed elitist and arrogant. However, I have said this before and I will say it again, the interaction of the doctor with patient is not simply *primum inter pares,* it should be knowledge and compassion on the one hand and trust on the other.

There is no clear exposition of this problem in law and no universally accepted code of best practice. A formula such as "all risks were discussed, all questions answered, informed consent given" should be unfailingly entered in the patient notes. It may provide at least some protection when the "wherefore you did mangle my client" letter arrives. The inevitable consequence of all of this is more defensive medicine and less productivity. If there is more law, there is less medicine. It is little wonder that St Luke is our patron saint.

> *Woe unto you lawyers! For you have taken away the day of knowledge*
> (Luke. 11:52)

June 21st, 2005

Horror health stories

Up the close and down the stair,
In the house with Burke and Hare,
Burke's the butcher Hare's the thief,
Knox, the man who buys the beef.

This children's rhyme came to mind because Sir Walter Scott's diary of January 28th, 1829 notes that Burke was hanged on that day before an immense crowd. The mob also bayed for the heads of Hare and Knox. Burke and Hare, both Irish, were making a few bob by selling bodies to Dr Knox for dissection. Grave robbing had become extremely difficult and was frowned upon in the best circles and our heroes, having made some money by selling a cadaver to Dr Knox, saw a gap in the market.

Their next logical step was to murder a few destitute people to keep the production line going. Like many money-making schemes it became unstuck when Dr Knox's medical students recognised some of the bodies including that of prostitute Mary Paterson. Hare turned King's evidence and his testimony convicted Burke who became the scapegoat for the macabre industry. Dr Knox was not charged but his career was effectively destroyed and indeed there was much clamour for his trial and execution.

This distressing incident put an end to the illicit trade in bodies and the British parliament moved to legalise the procurement of cadavers for dissection to abolish the black market trade. This was achieved by the Anatomy Act of 1832 which allowed unclaimed bodies, mostly from the workhouse, to be used for medical purposes. This effectively put the grave robbers out of business and there was no question of redundancy payments. The doctor, as usual, got off; nothing ever changes.

That's the bedtime story for today; useful if the children are proving a handful. I suppose it's illegal to tell them stories like that now as it will probably stunt their development rather than simply make them behave. Such will pass into history like the old fashioned clip in the ear. Is the world a better place?

I have lots of stories about the olden days and I have noticed that when I start, my listeners' eyes glaze over and they make a rapid exit. One advantage of writing a column is that I can't see the readers' eyes as I extol the virtues of the past.

I must say that whatever wondrous tales I can recount, I am sure that none will ever match the gothic horror tale of "Mary Harney and the Health Service". This will be guaranteed to put the frighteners on every man, woman and child in the country who can read. It also has the advantage of being a serial horror story, revealing fresh terrors every week.

I can see the chapter headings now; "Mary Harney overcomes the consultants", "Mary Harney slays the nurses", "Mary Harney vanquishes the GPs", "Mary Harney and the vanishing trolleys". I would hope the last chapter might be "Mary Harney wakes up", but I think this unlikely. I don't think the last line will be "and they all lived happily ever after". As for me I can't put it better than the Bible, "an horror of great darkness fell upon him" (Genesis).

I know there is an election coming and that we can expect all sorts of egregious nonsense. Mostly this does little harm but I suspect that this may not be the case this time. I feel great harm will come to the patients and to the morale of those providing the service by firmly establishing such an overt and unashamed two-tier service. What is proposed is nothing less. Don't forget folks, you will at some stage be the patients, this is no time for an "I'm all right Jack" approach. Why do you pay health insurance and what do you expect in return?

It is difficult to retain balance in this quicksand of contradictory nonsense and even writing about this floundering mess makes me angry. It seems from the perspective of those who have to provide the service that it is a case of "we're all out of step but our Mary". I hope I am wrong.

As I write, the debacle of the paediatric services unfolds. Yet another report says one major paediatric hospital near a general hospital and with good communications and easily accessible. We are to be told in two months. Common sense would indicate the Mater/Temple Street site, particularly as €46 million has already been invested in the site, planning permission obtained, and everything ready to go. More land, if required, should be available across the road when Mountjoy prison moves. Can anybody give a convincing reason why this should not be possible?

Let us have no wrangles between Government departments; they are all supposed to be working for the people. Can nobody in Government see the logic of proceeding on this site, rather than starting again from scratch? I was a Mater consultant and a consultant in Crumlin. There is inescapable logic in moving the paediatric cardiac surgical unit to this site which already houses the National Cardiac Surgical Unit.

Where is it to be? Who owns the land? Will it be built by the State or will it be another public/private partnership like the infamous M50? In the event of the hospital being elsewhere other than the Mater/Temple Street site, have we just kissed another €46 million goodbye? I think very many of us have had enough of arrogant costly incompetence. We will, however, have our day and we will not forget.

February 7th, 2006

19

Tomorrow there will be lots of jam

The rule is, jam tomorrow and jam yesterday - but never jam today.
Lewis Carroll, Through the Looking Glass.

This seems to be the current state of affairs. We are reminded constantly of all the benefits that have been bestowed on us lesser folk by our Ruling Elves. Many of these so called benefits, eg low taxation, do not bear close scrutiny, but the Rulers hold that if you repeat these things often enough, people will come to believe them. As for jam tomorrow, there is an election coming and we are going to be sick of jam of every possible variety by the time it is over. I await the menu to unfold although in truth, it has already begun.

"Never jam today" I would propose as the motto for the Minister for Trolleys and her acolytes, the HSE and the Department of Health. I am sure that the chief herald of Ireland could devise an armorial bearing that would encompass their sterling qualities and emphasise the chaos they have created. Solving the accumulated problems of the health service was never going to be easy and prompts a return to Through the Looking Glass: "If seven maids with seven mops, Swept it for half a year, "Do you suppose" the Walrus said, 'That they could get it clear? 'I doubt it' said the Carpenter, And shed a bitter tear."

Even when the seven maids were supplanted by a vast army of administrators, there was no hope of reform when those responsible chose and still choose to ignore the basic problem, pointed out repeatedly by doctors, nurses and those working with patients: There are not enough beds.

It was with frank incredulity that I heard the Minister for Trolleys declaim with a straight face that there is a crisis in the provision of A&E services and that this constitutes a national emergency. The same was repeated by the Taoiseach. I would like to thank you both for waking up, but it is not as simple as that. You both knew all along, and furthermore you ought to have known, that your feeble attempts at reform were not working. These reforms invariably called for "expert" groups to be set up to endlessly analyse the problems. Reports rather than reality are the hallmarks of recent incumbents of the Ministry for Trolleys. Brennan, Hanly and Prospectus etc, the list is endless. Needless to say, no action will be taken on any of the above with an election looming.

The many worthy folk who participated honestly in such planning must now wonder why they bothered. There is no contrition here, no admission that their plans and proposals have not worked and no acknowledgement that they were simply wrong. Instead there was double talk, obfuscation and denigration of those who pointed out the scandalous situation over which they presided, but apparently for which they bore no responsibility. There was talk of acute medical admissions units, talk of admission lounges. Both of these of course are merely what the nurses and doctors have been calling for - more beds. There were suggestions that if the doctors worked after 5.30pm, there would be no problem.

Acute hospitals never shut down and laboratory, radiology and medical services are always available. I have repeatedly pointed out that night and day exist even in hospitals and cannot be abolished by self-serving politicians seeking re-election. Likewise, GPs run evening surgeries and provide night cover in areas where such is safe. No amount of bluster, arrogance and bombast can conceal the fact that unsafe areas exist.

We are told of X number of patients who could be discharged, but have nowhere to go. We knew that. Whose responsibility is it to ensure that they have somewhere to go? It is again a matter of not enough places within the system to cope with the needs of the people and it is your responsibility.

There is no acknowledgement that the situation is further falsified by the National Treatment Purchase Fund buying patients off the waiting lists into private, for-profit institutions. This you have the gall to portray as success, when to any thinking person it simply points out the failure of the system over which you preside.

Population growth, increasing litigation and consequential defensive medicine, coupled with the removal of beds from the system, led inexorably to the situation in which we find ourselves now. No manipulations of figures and statistics can hide our failure to deliver a decent service to our people. Respected people have expressed in public their outrage at the situation and there has been a huge response from ordinary folk. Now there is an election looming.

What to do? Blame the doctors, Minister, a tried and true formula against a soft target. Maybe it was once, it will no longer do. I was very conscious when I wrote about the scandal in Drogheda that some folk would use it to attack my profession in general. It gives me no satisfaction to say that I was right.

Dr John Hillery in a moderate response to what I wrote stated that some might think that my point was against lay representation on the Medical Council. It was not, although with a lay majority it would cease to be a Medical Council. My point is that I feel the proposed plans for reform as laid out so far are unacceptable to the profession. The postulated use of agents provocateurs to quiz hard-working doctors is not merely unwise, it is contemptible. Those leading can easily become carried away by rhetoric and lose touch with their constituency. As for the politicians, the health service and the election, I quote Franklin D Roosevelt: "No man and no force can abolish memory."

April 4th, 2006

Nurses deserve fair pay

Last night I experienced again at first hand the A&E services in Dublin. I had occasion to bring a patient to St James's hospital as a semi emergency. It was a calm, efficient and well-organised unit, with an early separation of trauma and critically ill patients on the one hand, and what could be termed "the walking wounded" on the other. My patient belonged to the latter grouping, although the nature of the complaint required early assessment and/or treatment. This was done quickly, compassionately and carefully.

I cannot say enough for the professionalism, kindness and courtesy of all the frontline staff I met - porters, reception, nurses and doctors. This was cheerful and undaunted by an enormous work load, with patients requiring admission being transferred to the mandatory trolley.

At one stage a sister or staff nurse appeared to conduct a roll call of the waiting patients. She told everybody honestly that the waiting time for the less-than-critically ill was now eight hours before assessment. Clearly this was not the fault of herself and her fellow nurses; they were working non-stop. The assembled patients therefore accepted this stoically and with infinite patience. Alcohol and addiction did not seem to play a major role in this quiet group of the afflicted. I was assured, however, that this was a quiet evening and that it was early yet.

My heartfelt thanks to you all - the kind lady on reception, the nurses and doctors who looked after my emergency and all the other patients. You and your likes are all that keep this disgraceful service afloat.

Patricia Hewitt, Secretary of State in Britain's Department of Health and Social Services (DHSS), faced up to the nurses last week, to assert progress in the NHS. Such progress was not discernible to her angry audience and they made their displeasure felt. They lived with the reality, and no amount of obfuscation or grandiose claims would compensate them for the dismal present. At least Ms Hewitt had the guts to face them.

For our own Minister for Trolleys, there will be no ugly confrontation with the nurses of the Irish Nurses Organisation, as they gather for their annual conference. She has a prior meeting in America. As the INO conference is held in the same week every year and as no Minister has missed addressing this important group over the past 30 years, somebody was obviously very remiss in marking her diary. However, she sent them clear messages of her regard. As all your salaries have gone up by 60 per cent since 1997, your pay claim is not sustainable and will not be paid. Have a happy conference. PS You can forget about a Dublin allowance as well.

This is one of the oldest ploys in industrial relations. Sixty per cent rise, but 60 per cent of nothing is nothing. Just as well the nurses can't count. These are the silly folk who can't do their sums on the number of trolleys in each hospital every day. They keep getting it wrong and the better paid administrators who haven't been up all night have to do it for them.

As for the Dublin allowance, I honestly think that everybody would accept that they are a special group. As for the final pronouncement: "Well anyone that thinks I'm afraid of any group would want to think again."

My late father would have described this type of bravado as "whistling past the graveyard". Our nurses have been scandalously underpaid for years, Minister, and if you can divert your attention from establishing a right wing two-tiered health service for a few moments, you would see that this is indeed the case. Sadly, however, I am afraid that it will require someone bigger than you to do anything about it.

Meanwhile apparently, it is as Euripides put it circa 450 BC "It's better to be sick than nurse the sick. Sickness is single trouble for the sufferer: but nursing means vexation of the mind and hard work for the hands besides."

The Minister for Trolleys tells us that we are to have a lay majority on the Medical Council. She would have a role in the appointments but she stressed that it was not her intention to appoint her friends. Sure we know that Minister. Hasn't that always been the way in Irish political life? Aren't we long past that jobs for the boys attitude? Trouble is that whatever you call it; it will not be a Medical Council. I don't know any doctor who supports the proposal, even the President of the Council. But it needn't matter unduly.

The Minister for Trolleys isn't afraid of doctors, big ones, little ones, boys and girls; the bigger they are the harder they fall. In fact, she doesn't seem to be afraid of anyone. You had better watch out God, she might be after your job next; much as we would-hate to lose her.

May 9th, 2006

Beware of
pre-election time

Cry 'Havoc,' and let slip the dogs of war
(Julius Caesar, Act iii sc.1)

Maybe a bit melodramatic, but we have now entered into the period before a general election and there is one certain thing - those holding power do not relinquish it easily. This period almost amounts to a long interregnum in which paralysis in achievement is usually the most prominent feature. Do I hear somebody ask, "What's the difference between this period and the preceding years?" Frankly, I don't know, but I am sure some good things might have happened, if you look carefully enough.

This time is supposed to be characterised by suspension of our faculties of reason and understanding. It is a time in which the most outlandish promises are made by the competing elves and the above noted intellectual stagnation on our part leads us to believe them. Accordingly, in truth we deserve what we get. It is starting even now. Millions are to be spent on this, that, and the other. Every crackpot notion is to be facilitated; every single issue pressure group, no matter how precariously balanced on the lunatic fringe, is to be entertained.

Nobody is to be told to get lost. It is a time to be all things to all men - socialist, conservative, republican, liberal, and religious; whatever you're having yourself. No matter that all of this is contradictory. That stupid shower (us) won't notice. So long as they have enough for a foreign holiday, a few circuses (football matches), a few pints and they can pay the mortgage, they'll think we're great. When we throw in the SSIAs at the crucial time, sure we're laughing. If only some of that miserable shower of civil servants would get the finger out over their decentralisation, we'd be fixed rightly.

Time to wake up folks and take a good hard look at where we stand now. Have we squandered the Celtic Tiger? Letting the good times roll now is hardly a blueprint for harder times ahead. Could some lesser elf in Government, at the risk of losing his head, ask the leadership if by any chance they are losing the run of themselves? Could they point out to them that the natives are getting restless?

This particular native is restless and has been for a long time. His disquiet is not allayed in any measure by recent happenings. He finds it difficult to believe the recent legal debacle just kind of happened and that, as usual, nobody is to blame. He wonders about the grasp on reality of those who tell us that nothing could have been done about it once the process was in train. An outraged public response forced a quick 'volte face' here.

Then they acted quickly enough, albeit minus the chief elf who was lecturing the world about HIV/Aids, instead of being at home minding our little shop. Has it dawned on them yet that the populace would much rather a government to be proactive rather than sluggishly reactive?

But in any case, reaction there was, and Mr A is back in prison. We have passed new laws and although I am no lawyer I would tend to agree with those who predict trouble to ensue from this hurried legislation. How can you treat a 17-year-old boy and girl differently in these times of equality? If what we have seen constitutes a "measured response" to the problem, then God help the children and the young in our society. We have failed children in this State before; let us not do so again.

Since I am on the subject of children, I commend the HSE for a decision on the location of the new children's hospital. This was a decision that was never going to please everybody, no matter what location had been chosen. About €56 million had already been spent on the Mater site and it is good to see it is not being wasted. The Rotunda Hospital is due to relocate there in another positive and progressive move. Accordingly, it is disappointing to note the reaction of some of the disappointed groups. I would have thought such protests ring hollow in view of the agreed urgency of proceeding with this project quickly.

I understand the Mater put forward a logical and detailed plan for the development, covering not only the medical end, but also matters of access and parking. I think it would now be proper to publish this to allay the fears of the doubters and disgruntled. I think it is vital that we now have a time scale and costing. Let us have answers and movement now.

This is a rational move and hopefully one of a series that will examine the distribution of medical specialties logically across the State and act rationally to provide the best service. That won't be popular either.

For the record, I was a consultant in both the Mater and Our Lady's Hospital and I do not believe that this decision was made for anything but sound medical reasons, certainly not for political advantage. I also feel that Noel Smyth's generous offer should be gratefully accepted; such philanthropy should be lauded, appreciated, and encouraged. Stirring times lie ahead.

June 13th, 2006

Stopping squander mania

I had hoped that some of my friends might see their way to giving me a dig out in the coming year. It's not that I want it for anything in particular, but a few nice meals wouldn't come amiss, and the Highest Authority tells me I need some new shirts. Mind you, most of my friends are a tight lot and do not let the Communion money go lightly. Besides there's not much I can give them in return. I can't appoint them to anything.

There's a bit in Emma Lazarus's poem inscribed on the plinth of the Statue of Liberty that goes "Give your tired, your poor, your huddled masses yearning to break free." This came to mind the other day, as there was a huddled mass on the Rock Road. This consisted of about 10 chaps huddled together and as far as the eye could judge, not apparently doing anything. Mind you, in fairness, it was raining and they were engaged in the serious business of the perpetual road works on the Rock Road.

I declare an interest immediately. I live on this road and my blood pressure and coronary arteries are tested on a daily basis by this incomprehensible shambles.

For over a year now it has been excavated, repaired, re-piped, etc. The water has been cut off, reconnected and cut off again and generally the citizens treated as if their inconvenience was a matter of scant regard.

Refuse collections and recycling collections are totally screwed up. Our little cul de sac has a harmless little game of "guess the bin day". It is great fun. It has also made street cleaning impossible and so this major thoroughfare is littered with debris of every imaginable kind.

The end result was inevitable, literally unceasing gridlock. Gallons of fuel expended and the poor old globe warmed even further. Other roads from south Dublin were in turn overwhelmed by motorists fleeing from this madness. I am talking here about ordinary motorists, not criminals. People who want to drive their car from A to B on their own business. People who naively think that in return for their taxes, on fuel, on cars and in general, that the State would facilitate the necessary travel; people who now know that the State doesn't give a damn.

Two final points on this topic: firstly, no work was done on this project at nights or weekends despite this being one of the busiest roads in the country; secondly, work now appears to be suspended to facilitate Operation Freeflow. Glue flows more freely. We all have our traffic war stories to tell from all around the country. Why do we put up with it? PS There doesn't seem to be a forwarding address for the huddled mass.

So one aspiration is that the road will become passable again sometime soon. A second aspiration is that Bupa will stay. Anybody who reads this column knows my feelings about the current state of the health service. Against all the odds I have the pious hope that 2007 might bring new ideas and new faces to this beleaguered service. The insurance debacle beggars belief.

Competition, seemingly, is just a word, nothing to believe in. No company could ever compete with the VHI monopoly, given so called "risk equalisation". Somebody might be able to live with community rating, dubious concept that it is, but no company could live with handing over its profit to a competitor.

In time Bupa's client base will age, as will that of Vivas, VHI will acquire new younger clients and the market will adjust. Meantime, the newer companies have to meet the statutory levels of insurance reserves, incredibly the VHI does not, until 2012.

Mind you, the VHI reserves were not helped by being plundered by Government as a short-term expedient. Once again, it was neither VHI money nor Government money, but the subscribers' money; once again we did nothing.

What have we now? A monopoly health insurer and scads of new private hospitals fuelled by tax breaks. This is an intolerable situation, particularly for the patients who are deprived of the most basic right, that of choice. What ever happened the Competition Authority, or was that only to chase lawyers and doctors?

I would like 2007 above all to be remembered as the year in which we collectively rediscovered the word value. It has for some years little meaning in this country. Value for money was a concept that decreed that what you got for your outlay was clearly worth it. We all understood that. It doesn't apply any more. If you doubt this, just look at the housing market.

Prices three and four times the real value of the property are tolerated by us just to get a roof over our heads. Governments are supposed to protect the people and not let such shameless exploitation occur. In all of this we are the losers. Guess who gains? Let me not be too cynical, it's not all bad news. You might get a job sweeping the tent.

Let's make a statement in 2007 that we want better health and education services, that we want better roads and housing, that we want value for money and above all that we want accountability and responsibility. Let us have an end to squander mania. Let us have value.

Honoré de Balzac wrote "L'avarice commence où la pauvreté cesse" or "Greed begins where poverty ends". Not here it doesn't, Honoré, in this island of saints and scholar's they live comfortably side by side.

January 2nd, 2007

31

Layered in secrecy

For secrets are edged tools
And must be kept from children and from fools
(John Dryden)

Possibly many of the problems regarding the concept, siting and development of the new children's hospital derive from the layers of secrecy with which the project has been shrouded. The children, of course, are seen not to count and the rest of us answer for the fools.

This is a very big project, very costly, and with long-term consequences for the wellbeing of the nation's children. We would all like to know that everything about it is above board, that the right location has been chosen and why. We would like to know the basis for this choice and the opinions of those consulted. It may well be that the right choice has been made; so let's know everything. It is our entitlement.

I suppose it was a mixture of cowardice and the simple desire to lead a quiet life, which has largely kept me out of this controversy. Now I find that writing this column places me in a difficult position.

For over 25 years I was a consultant cardiac surgeon in the Mater hospital (the National Cardiac Surgical Unit) and also in Our Lady's Hospital for Sick Children in Crumlin. In both fine institutions I have very many great friends. If, in my hopeless endeavour to sit on the fence, I find that like Horace, "Brevis esse laboro, obscurus fio" (I try to be clear, but am merely obscure), you will understand my predicament.

A couple of things bother me about the initial process. Firstly, why did we need McKinseys, worthy as they may be, to carry out this audit? Have we not got enough experience inhouse? Secondly, how much did it cost? It seemed to have been completed in a very short time. These are legitimate questions, no place for secrecy. However derived, the conclusion that the needs of children would be best served by one centre of excellence was accepted by all interested parties. This was merely the calm before the storm as any prescient observer of the Irish medical shambles could have foretold.

It is my understanding that each contending site made a submission to the deciding body as to its suitability for the location of the new hospital. I believe that all intimated that they would accept wherever was chosen. It is not clear if the possibility of a standalone, state-of-the-art facility on a greenfield site was ever considered. If not, why not?

We were told that the new hospital should be co-located with an adult teaching hospital. We were not told why nor by whom. Many frontline children's hospitals are not so situated and manage very well indeed. Furthermore, it was suggested that there should be a maternity hospital also on site. Our children's hospitals have survived for very many years without this premise. What is the necessity for this now?

In the same way that the adult teaching hospitals made their submissions to the group, I presume the paediatric hospitals did likewise. If not, I simply cannot understand why they have waited until now, when the decision, for better or for worse, has been made and the process was moving forward. The answer of course is the fact that some liked the chosen location and some did not. The result: threats and blusters and cries of "we're not playing any more".

The problem here is that they don't own the ball and there's no point in running to Mammy, because she has firmly indicated that she is not for turning. Less firm apparently was the Taoiseach who is said to have had misgivings about the chosen location. I am alive long enough to be extremely sceptical about these "misgivings". I would rather think that this is merely an effort to keep everybody onside until after the election. "Ah, you never know what'll happen, sure nothing's decided finally yet," classically accompanied by a wink, but in this case not by a nod. The Cabinet, no less, is standing firm on this decision; "let yiz all shut up now". I ask myself, where in the world would the cabinet in a democracy become involved in an issue such as this?

But there are serious questions to be answered. It is alleged that the deciding body contained no working paediatricians and that the level of consultation with the involved children's hospitals was minimal. It is alleged that overseas experts consulted on the format gave no preference for any particular site. We were subtly led to believe that they were somehow involved, and that this was not merely a home town decision. Sadly such dissembling would be par for the course.

Many other questions have been raised and not answered. Who is right about the access to the various sites, and in any case does this matter very much? No matter where you go, someone is going to feel aggrieved and boy, aren't we great ones for a sense of grievance?

We don't know about room sizes, parents' accommodations, play areas, light considerations, green areas, etc. Give us all an idea and commitment as soon as possible. Remember, no secrets, no silences, because rumour and misinformation fill the gaps. In any case, this is going to be a long time coming, wherever, if ever it is. Let us give credit only when the doors open and the petty rivalries are left behind.

I must confess that I do not see agreement on any chosen adult site within the city. They must all be, as Dr Pat Doherty of Crumlin put it, "suboptimal". Lastly, the provision of the soon- to-be-vacated (?) site of Mountjoy to the Mater site would seem to answer most questions. Is this too obvious?

January 23rd, 2007

Left with little after plenty

Yesterday was as if winter had returned, cold and wet with a bitter wind from the north-west. It did not seem right to turn on the heating in July but it was either that or freeze. There is little of the stoic in me and hence the house soon warmed. Twelve hours later there was a complete transformation; breakfast outdoors on a warm sunny morning, followed by a swim on a rising tide. I felt that the world had returned to normal and that things were ordained as they should be. Sadly I knew that to be a delusion.

I have been intrigued by other delusions. "We must not talk ourselves into a recession." One may ask to whom this refers. Some years ago I wondered what would happen when the cranes of Ireland's building boom started to fly away. To me this seemed inevitable, and so it has proved. I wonder how it is that I, a doctor, and thousands like me in all walks of life could clearly see this coming and yet those responsible for running the State could not and apparently still cannot. Many, including this writer, have pointed out for years that we are over reliant on the construction industry and that in the medium to long term this was not sustainable.

We are now told that employment in home construction can be switched to the infrastructural undertakings of the National Development Plan. Maybe some can, much cannot and in any case the funding of the NDP is predicated on growth rates in the economy which are unlikely to be realised. Now we are being told we must not talk ourselves into trouble. We are being told this by those whose short-sighted actions, or worse, indolent inaction led us dismally in this doleful direction.

Yesterday I received a letter from an American doctor in Connecticut telling me that the house of a late colleague which was for sale had been reduced in price to $525,000 or less than €400,000. It had 20 acres, a large pond, mature trees, a perfectly maintained colonial house c.1740, approximately 2,500 square feet and one and a half hours from New York. On a recent visit to Ireland this Irish American had entertained the idea of purchasing a property here. He was appalled at the prices for even the most mediocre houses. He sent me the above, as he put it "a reality check" and wondered "if you folk never heard of the word, value".

Our now ailing, but not yet moribund Celtic Tiger made some inordinately wealthy and created an illusion of national prosperity. Benjamin Disraeli writing of similar times in our neighbouring isle wrote: "In those days England was for the few, and for the very few." I am afraid that it has been so here also. Increasing inflation and energy prices, rising interest rates and consequent mortgage increases, the endeavours to maintain private health insurance in view of a failed health service; all these place intolerable burdens on ordinary mortgage-paying citizens struggling to stay afloat in increasingly choppy waters. Betty Jane Wylie wrote: "Poverty isn't being broke; poverty is never having enough." It is into this limbo that many are being propelled by rising costs on all sides.

My worst enemy would not accuse me of being a Marxist, but Karl Marx wrote a lot of sense too. "The devaluation of the human world increases in direct relation with the increase in value of the world of thing." Materialism is very much the creed of our times. This is coupled with blind unthinking hope that the good times will roll forever. The breakfast roll man of David McWilliams probably epitomised this in the recent election. This genus and indeed many others seem to live on the basis of carpe diem. It seems to go unnoticed that we have to produce goods and sell them in a very competitive world market, one that appreciates and requires value.

In many areas, including vital ones like tourism, we do not give value. We know this but we seem to do nothing about it. There is no leadership from the top. Quite the opposite indeed as the citizenry are scarcely edified with secret deals with backbenchers designed to keep the Government in power, additional junior ministerial appointments (needed like the proverbial hole in the head), and innumerable placemen installed. It matters not a whit that some of these lucky folk have no discernible or relevant ability for the posts they may fill. It's jobs for the boys, business as usual.

We are told that we are creating a "knowledge-based economy". Fine words indeed and would this was true. Inadequate investment at all educational levels and particularly in the university sector gives the lie to this platitudinous deception.

The getting and holding of power at all costs is what it is all about, and this is not commensurate with the common weal. Nonetheless, the pressures now crowding from all sides are going to make it very hard for our own Houdini with his three election trick, to square this particular circle. Meanwhile, the rest of us who should be enjoying the fruits of our much vaunted economic success; a superb educational system, wonderful hospitals, whatever you can think of yourself, the trappings of a modern caring society, are left with but a pittance and the certainty of harder times coming.

In the good times unfortunately there was neither the will nor the ability to ensure the future. We could power windmills with endless talk and discussion; now the time for talking is over. We require action to salvage what we can.

July 17th, 2007

38

Constant stream of waffle

Pass me my Zimmerframe and let's go. I laughed out loud at the Taoiseach's portrayal of me as some sort of one time, homicidal geriatric. The many, many years of retirement are actually five, and I don't think I'm senile quite yet. You never know though, the Highest Authority thinks maybe I am becoming a little forgetful. But I'm not alone in that, Taoiseach?

My interest was also aroused by your sincere felicitations to the consultant who had a big private practice as well as his public commitment. I can tell you how that happens. He was probably very good at his job and patients wanted to go to him and doctors referred to him. That's how the old order worked. But it did work.

I have been writing recently about the insidious notion that if standard business practices are applied to medicine, things will get better. This was the principle behind the establishment of the Health Management Organisations (HMOs) in America and indeed other private healthcare systems there. There is a certain simple plausibility about it, and worryingly some signs of its adoption here. Classically it comes in three phases:

1. Over promise: We will give you everything you need - liver, heart, lung transplants, perpetual dialysis. No need to wait in A&E departments. And consultants will look after you even if you need only an aspirin. We will establish centres of excellence and we'll diagnose, treat and cure everything with no mistakes. We'll be data driven by the latest information technology and we will employ only evidence-based medicine.

2. Under fund: Jesus! This is costing a fortune. We can't go on like this. We have to get out of it somehow. Let's tell them that there's a slight delay, due to planning and consultation with the social partners. Tell them any old mumbo-jumbo. Slip it in that that's the reason we need such well-paid managers and bonuses. They'll understand the strains we must be under. Tell them it's their fault anyway for protesting about lousy service; distracting our gaze from the bright horizon of a world class health service so ardently desired by the Minister for Trolleys. Do anything, ration services, deny care, stifle everything in bureaucracy. Let them die; it's cheaper. Screw the complainers and the doctors.

3. Shift the blame: They are on to us! It's those greedy doctors who are causing the problems. The bloody nurses are out of control. The pharmacists, dentists, whoever, are robbing the nation blind. Repeat ad nauseam; it's not our fault, but just keep voting for us and paying up and things will get better.

Will they? This retired, ancient, ex potential assassin doesn't think so at all. I think that things can only go from "mad to worse".

This newspaper recently carried an article headlined "Shorter stay, more free beds". This was based on an interview with the national director of the HSE's Winter Initiative Plan. I think that's kind of equal to a Field Marshall and paid and bonused accordingly. Put firmly out of your heads any notional similarity to Napoleon's march on Moscow and the eventual outcome of that debacle. This is the real thing. Please don't laugh; concentrate. Like all emanations from this organisation it is very strong on aspiration. There is grand talk about expanding and developing community healthcare measures that would eliminate the need for some hospital admissions and provide a suitable home care package for discharged patients. It waffles on and on.

The spokesman is quoted as saying, "we're not saying this can happen overnight". Ah yes, put it with the centres of excellence, the cancer strategy, the primary care strategy and whatever the multiplicity of "advisers" and spin doctors can dream up for our grateful approval.

Meanwhile, back on planet Earth, in Ireland we are actually reducing patient services. Minister Cowen tells us we can expect little more money for State services next year, other than covering inflation. We know what that means.

There's more; "increasing the capability of diagnostic facilities such as radiology and laboratories by 25 per cent would result in a 6 per cent increase in total inpatient discharges". Wonderful, just tell that to the hospitals with diminishing staff numbers, old equipment and a moratorium on improving the situation. Don't ask why basic services are being shipped out of the State at this time, cervical smear testing for example. Just more talk and deception, I'm afraid.

We are being compared with countries that have far better infrastructure and community facilities than we have. That's why our patients spend a little longer in hospital. No doctor wants to discharge patients into an unsuitable environment where help is not at hand.

November 13th, 2007

On the road to nowhere, very slowly

National stress day or anti-stress day or whatever it was, found me driving from Limerick to Dublin on the N7. It was morning and the traffic was moderate. Just on the Dublin side of Birdhill matters slowed appreciably and I joined an eastbound slow convoy at about 30mph. I speculated idly on the cause of the stagnation, just possibly it might be one of the National Roads Authorities mobile "traffic calming" devices, ie, the ubiquitous tractor. Traffic passing in the opposite direction appeared unhindered and proceeded at a normal pace. I speculated on the cause of our continuing obstruction and shared my thoughts with the Highest Authority. In retrospect perhaps I sounded a trifle irritated. "What's the hurry," she inquired calmly, reading the paper, "we'll get there sometime." And this said on national bloody stress day, mind you!

I settled back as we crawled towards Nenagh. The occasional van and car dropped out of the procession ahead and I drew closer to whatever was causing the obstruction. Eventually I got a clear view ahead. "Jesus Christ," I prayed;

drawing another rebuke from the HA, "would you look at that." There, weaving in the middle of the road like some sort of demented Pied Piper, was a learner driver under instruction. The driver paid no notice to her fellow citizens going about their presumably lawful business and queuing up for miles astern; moving over to facilitate safe overtaking was not a thought entertained. The instructor might have been asleep or possibly just scared rigid.

Again I requested the HA to view this doleful tableau, in which she evinced little interest. "Where are the traffic corps?" I demanded. "I don't know," she responded testily. "Why don't you ask them yourself?" "I'll tell you where they are," I said. "They're sitting on the Rock Road, waiting for some criminal to make a break down the bus lane." She pointedly ignored me. But deliverance was at hand. The Pied Piper lurched left towards Nenagh and those liberated behind thankfully headed for the bypass. This was down to one lane for nearly its entire length.

Count to 10, my mother used to advise; I tried and it didn't work. It wasn't that I was in a particular hurry or going anywhere special. It was just an old fashioned notion that we ought to be able to travel the roads unhindered and at a reasonable rate. This was the snail racing segment. The wall of death part came later near the appropriately named townland of Kill, where the roadway divided into two separate passages; an adjacent notice invited you to select either. I selected the outer or left hand lane. It definitely wasn't my day. I found myself in a narrow strait, crash barriers on either side a good foot away from the car. Immediately to my left the traffic thundered southwards; the big articulated trucks shaking my flimsy little car. I wondered why this particular motorway has been under construction for half of my adult life.

Finally after further adventures at the Red Cow roundabout, I reached home; a broken man. The HA yawned, stretched and said, "there now, that wasn't too bad was it?" I felt an immediate affinity with the luckless wedding guest in Coleridge's Ancient Mariner;

He went like one that had been stunned
And is of sense forlorn

A sadder and a wiser man,
He rose the morrow morn.

National Stress Day my ass; whoever dreamt that one up; bet you it had something to do with the HSE.

Since I am on wheels, I might as well continue. I am the owner of a Garmin Satellite Navigator Direction finder gifted to me by one of the Lesser Authorities. The quid pro quo apparently is that I pay for her wedding. Seems fair enough the way these things go. Recently while driving, being guided by Mrs Garmin's rather bossy voice, the phone rang in the car. My caller asked if by any chance the HA was with me. I pointed out that the voice he had heard was Mrs Garmin telling me where to go. His was an understandable mistake. I might also have noted that the only phrase missing from the Mrs Garmin repertoire viz a vis the HA seems to be "why didn't you just stop and ask somebody?"

Rumours are abroad that we are to get a Green budget and that owners of gas guzzlers and SUVs are to pay for their sins in bringing the world to the brink of destruction. My sceptical little mind suggests that if we had no more traffic logjams on our inadequate road system, we would save as much in fuel consumption and emissions. How about getting rid of the cows instead, aren't they a major part of the problem?

Seriously though, this is a problem. The people who drive such vehicles paid for them with higher VRT, VAT, they pay higher Road Fund Tax and they contribute more tax on their petrol or diesel consumption. They bought their vehicles in good faith and now it seems they are to be retrospectively taxed. Furthermore, the resale value of such cars would be negligible, compounding the iniquity of this proposal. Emissions from such vehicles are in any case a tiny part of the global warming problem.

This is rather about polishing up a tarnished Green image on the one hand; and screwing more tax out of us on the other. Anybody who believes such a meaningless gesture will save the planet is possessed of an innocence that I truly envy. Time to sign off now as I have to go to my light bulb changing class.

November 27th, 2007

44

There's money to be made in this system

But money answereth all things
(Ecclesiastes 10:19)

It's all about money. I was very slow to realise that. We simply need more money for the health system. But that poses a problem: where do we get it? We can try saving on an already inadequate spend, a bit like getting blood out of a stone, in medical metaphor. Consider closing a few hospitals and stopping a few services, maybe? But no, you're right, we've been doing that for ages and things are only getting worse.

How about increasing the money for the HSE and the Department of Health? Don't even start whining about black holes, good money after bad, etc - we've heard it all before. We could consider increasing tax; that always goes down well with folks who imagine they'll never be sick. They're the same ones, by the way, who lead the charge when a doctor screws up or a hospital falls down. No, you don't think that would run? Let's try again.

Did you ever hear of a little word called rationalisation? We could try in a small way by cutting out overheads such as bonuses, and trips to the Superbowl in the Government jet. Yes, I know, it wasn't really for that, it was for a one-day course on how best to provide cancer and dental services. Gosh, weren't the rest of us slow learners?

It took us ages. In the same vein - and quietly - maybe somebody could unravel all the layers of administration and find out exactly what they do. Maybe we could do without a small proportion of them, about 60 to 70 per cent. Maybe, though, rationalisation is a bit grandiose. Perhaps it's better if things actually don't make any sense and remain fuzzy around the edges. That way, it's hard to identify who is responsible for the latest calamity. God forbid that anybody might be fired or have to resign. This is the Republic of Ireland; we don't do that kind of thing here. I'll bet you Little Ian wishes he was down here.

I'm not having much success filling the coffers, am I? How about reducing salaries for doctors, nurses, dentists and paramedics? Maybe we could filch a few bob from the pharmacists? We could reduce the working day. I know the new contract says we're going to extend it but that's only for the consumption of the plebs. How could we do that without spending more? Get a grip, will you?

I'm still not doing very well. Maybe I should start "thinking outside the box". Of course, I realise that this can only be done on "a level playing field, going forward, from this point in time". Maybe it's not just the patients who need the speech therapists. I'd like to borrow one from the HSE but I gather they've been abolished.

Let's have some practical suggestions. How about a charge for occupying a trolley, say €5 per hour? You could charge €2 for a chair and €1 for standing, or sitting on the floor. I've thought this through. There would be a maximum trolley time of six hours, and after that your trolley would be clamped. The fee for removing the clamp would be €50 and each additional hour thereafter would be at a rate of €10.

Use of the toilet would be €5, with €1 remitted if you scrubbed the floor or changed a lightbulb. There would, of course, be a €5 charge for somebody to mind your trolley while you are in the loo. Room service on the trolley would be €30 with an extra €1 if you want a glass of water. What do you mean a cup of tea? Do you think we're running a hotel? I nearly forgot, use of a bedpan would be €10.

The possibilities are endless. If you had family members in the A&E department with you they could be liable to a congestion charge and there would be a booking charge if you wanted visitors in the hospital.

You could even get a few of the walking wounded to sit huddled on the pavement outside the hospital with little paper cups shaking them at passers-by. They could have little placards saying: "Spare €1 for the ultrasound." There are no limits to the money to be made - I told you it was easy.

March 4th, 2008

Freedom of speech held dear by all

The barometer has resumed its downward march and the rain and wind are unremitting. I have an uneasy feeling that this summer may be a carbon copy of last year. I feel sympathy with those folk being transmitted around the Ring of Kerry on coach tours; as of today they could see little of the spectacular scenery. I can scarcely see across the estuary back towards the Ring. It is definitely a day when one has a licence to be lazy.

It has been an interesting week. I have a clear conscience on Lisbon. I voted yes, but I can readily understand why many folk did not. I don't know what happens next. Would a referendum across all 27 states be possible? This would refute or confirm that resistance to the treaty is widespread and not just confined to the perverse Paddies. Then we would all know and subsequent action would be based on an unequivocal democratic mandate.

The debate, however, has been sidelined by more pressing domestic issues.

We seem to be now officially in recession. I heard somebody recently allude to the Celtic Lemmings who followed the good times without ever pausing to wonder if the cliff edge was near. They would be akin to the Celtic Ostrich who pretended it wasn't happening.

Smugly, I claim a clear conscience here also. I have been writing about this probability for over five years. It gives me no pleasure to see this unpleasant situation come to pass. I would much rather have been wrong. This is the more galling in that the fruits of our undoubtedly good times, however germinated, have been squandered, leaving disastrous legacies in health, education and basic infrastructure.

Now, seemingly, we are being asked to believe that those whose lack of foresight, or even indifference to the clearly discernible consequences of their actions, are the very people best qualified to lead us back to firmer ground. I have some difficulty with this proposition.

> *By thy long grey beard and glittering eye*
> *Now wherefore stoppst thou me?*
> (Samuel Taylor Coleridge – 'The Rime of the Ancient Mariner')

I'll tell you why I was stopped. I had the temerity to cast a little doubt on the latest sacred cow, ie global warming. I am sceptical about many aspects of this and the rolling waves of orthodoxy that seek to engulf us all. Apparently, I am heretical, although I am comforted by the thought that they don't burn heretics any more as that would only contribute further to such warming. However, there are other ways to put the recalcitrant in place.

A writer to this paper referred to my poor understanding of this issue and characterised my poor utterances as "pub talk". I had not heard this phrase for many years. It used to be a favourite of my late mother. I don't know why I assumed the writer castigating me was some sage weighed with age, knowledge and experience. This kind soul, while acknowledging that I may have been okay as a surgeon, goes on to warn me "that future generations may not be grateful to those who use their influence to obstruct necessary behavioural change to reduce our carbon emissions. The cost of getting it wrong is too great to trivialise this subject".

He then goes on to solemnly warn me that "the future of the human species on earth is at stake". Bless my soul, I didn't realise that one little column could consign us all to oblivion. However, there was a hint of "betwixt the stirrup and the ground, mercy was sought and mercy found". All was not lost, the writer sincerely hopes "that I will acquaint myself better with this topic in the hope that he will revisit it in a future column and undo the damage he has caused".

Wow, I didn't realise I laboured under the delusion that the readers of this newspaper were mature enough to make up their own minds on issues like this. They will know that this irresponsible columnist is very far from being alone in harbouring legitimate doubts concerning this topic. I dare say that many would feel that changing light bulbs, banning bonfires and corking cows are pathetic, indeed banal answers, to the perceived problem.

Freedom of thought and opinion, speech and expression are fundamentals held dear by all. So back to 'The Rime of the Ancient Mariner'.

Hold off! Unhand me greybeard loon!

I'll do my own little thing.

July 1st, 2008

Co-located hospitals - a sound investment?

The Irish Medical Times headline of August 29th, 2008 reads: "Co-located hospitals credit crunch." In discussing funding implications for their development and listing some of the entrepreneurial names involved, it quotes Tom Finn, assistant national director of the HSE's National Hospitals Office (wow), as follows: "Clearly it would be foolish to think the current climate will not have an effect, but banks have to lend money to stay in business, ultimately the co-locations will be banked and they will come to fruition within two or three years. I don't have any doubts about that."

I would not invest in a co-located hospital, nor would I support any financial institution that chose to do so. Quite apart from any moral considerations, and these are many, I would consider it a bad investment, on fiscal grounds.

This divisive scheme, based upon an absurd plan to "free up private beds in public hospitals", is founded on the same types of tax breaks that have already created havoc in our economy. We may be slow learners, but for God's sake hopefully we're not that slow. Look around you and note the half-empty hotels, unsold apartments and houses, and unlet commercial premises which stand as monuments to collective Governmental folly.

It is seemingly of no consequence to the Minister and her teeming cohorts that those decanted from the public beds to these ill-defined and uncosted entities have in fact every statutory right to the beds they currently occupy. Likewise, it did not seem obvious to these genii that the provision of a mere 30 beds per existing hospital could achieve the same result. It is also ignored that 1,000 beds is not nearly enough to meet the needs of a vastly increased and ageing population.

On practical grounds, however, there are compelling reasons one should not invest in such nebulous institutions. Any such hospital needs a volume of paying patients to survive and repay its development costs, let alone develop further.

Oh! And let's not forget the real reason - to make a profit. Such patients are insured either personally, or through employment-based group schemes, with the VHI, Vivas or similar. Some patients are paid for by the National Treatment Purchase Fund (NTPF). Overseas patients and those paying from disposable income constitute a negligible minority.

Lest we forget, we already have a group of excellent private hospitals which, between them, account for most of the hospital expenditure of the insurance groups. It is no secret, either, that some of these hospitals would go out of business were it not for the artificial prop of the NTPF. This half-baked concept was conceived in good times, no matter how artificially contrived. Now, indisputably, our prosperity is not increasing. We are in, or very close to, recession.

The problems arising are legion, and only the very rich are untroubled by the negative consequences of our present situation. This obviously has an impact on activities such as private hospital developments shielded by iniquitous tax breaks. In such times the pool of insured patients, currently more than 50 per cent of the population, is not going to grow. It is going to contract as some of those currently insured lose their jobs or emigrate.

Many folk faced with inexorable increases in the cost of living, including the cost of health insurance, will take an unhappy but hard look at all aspects of discretionary spending.

Others, struggling around the minimum wage, those on fixed barely adequate pensions, those unemployed or disabled have no such dilemmas. They are dependent on what the State has inadequately provided in services, which in the current climate are not going to improve. The potential patients of these institutions have choices. They are hardly likely to forgo mortgage payments and lose their houses. This would be the last option.

What comes next - smaller cars, a single car, and no car? Overseas holidays and even overseas property are dispensable. What about private school fees? What about private health insurance? There are many more smaller discretionary items which will be jettisoned as the economy and personal circumstances contract. Do we leave the golf club or the gym or whatever? Individuals and families will exercise different options.

Some will choose to let health insurance go, rationalising that they are entitled to free hospital cover anyway. This is happening already, and will become more obvious as subscriptions reach renewal dates. Some will reduce cover. A fall in numbers and a lessening of cover will, of course, inhibit the ability of the insurers to fund the postulated "pig in a poke" co-locations. That part of the equation is simple.

The other part of the equation is equally simple. There are, and have been for many years past, major cutbacks in medical services. There are increasing and inequitable inadequacies.

Nobody believes the "there will be no cutbacks in frontline services" mantra of the HSE and this discredited Minister. The people can see for themselves. Accordingly, the other proposed prop of co-location looks distinctly shaky.

Lastly, the Minister responsible for this grievously socially divisive measure tells developers and potential investors: "You're on your own lads, we'll not be bailing you out."

No, I wouldn't invest in co-located hospitals.

September 2nd, 2008

Barack, I'm not exactly twinkletoes either

Dear Barack, You don't know me, but I thought I would write to you because there is a strong bond between us. Apparently, the First Lady of the United States shares with my Highest Authority a poor opinion of our capabilities on the dance floor and has shared these with the public at large. I understand this upset you. I know exactly how you feel. I think it's something about co-ordinating the music with the steps if that's any help to you.

I wouldn't worry too much about it, women can be quite insensitive about these things and we're not meant to have feelings. In any case I'm sure you'll have lots of other things to do.

Meanwhile, Barack, don't be worrying about us over here in Ireland. We're doing fine and we're even going to restore your ancestral castle in Moneygall. In fact, the citizens of the town are considering bestowing the ultimate Irish accolade upon you and naming a pub in your honour. That's some metropolis you spring from Mr President.

According to PW Joyce in his seminal work Irish Names of Places, Moneygall translated from the original Irish means "shrubbery of the strangers". Sounds a bit odd that, maybe it's a prophecy of some sort.

Why your Kearney ancestor left such a fascinating place is not quite clear. There is an Irish song which may throw some light on this conundrum;

> For sure's me name is Kearney
> I'll be off to Californey
> And instead of digging praties
> I'll be digging lumps of gold.

This was written by the late Peadar Kearney, composer of our National Anthem and uncle of Brendan Behan. God knows who else you might be related to.

It gets better. Apparently further back one of your ancestors was Michael Kearney who ran a prosperous wig-making business in Dublin in the 1700s. He also had extensive property interests. He is reputed to have banked with Anglo Irish bank.

It all went belly up at the time of the great property crash brought about by the Act of Union in 1800 and at the same time wigs went out of fashion. He possibly fled his creditors and wound up in Moneygall; like the way the lads now wind up in Lichtenstein or the Bahamas.

Before disaster struck he had found time to become Master of the Dublin guild of Barber Surgeons. That's my crowd, Mr President, only now they call themselves the Royal College of Surgeons in Ireland. I maybe shouldn't have put that bit in Barack, because they'll probably be after you now for a few dollars. They'd get blood out of a stone that lot!

Moneygall, when your folks left wouldn't have been exactly a barrel of laughs. It had 76 houses and 379 people in King's County (Offaly now, since we got rid of the Brits) and near the border with Tipperary. There were three fairs a year and there was a police station. That's about it, so it's not surprising the wanderlust stirred. I am a regular bird of passage through the town on my way to Kerry and have been known to stop there. They've got a bit of work to do to spruce it up a bit for your expected visit.

By chance, the town lies in the fiefdom of our Chief Elf, Brian the Bold, or as some begrudgers call him "Biffo the Bad". Be duly respectful Barack, this great figure earns more than you and is renowned throughout the land for his fairy stories. In fact, Moneygall could well be chosen as the situation for his library which will contain the complete collection of fairy tales from his party and will in time rival the Book of Kells . It is simply titled Tales from the Tent .

There is a little problem. This concerns medical facilities. The local dispensary was established in 1826 and the primary care is provided by the GP practice; the backbone of Irish medicine. If some minor ailment strikes one of your group, you'll be grand. If something more serious, God forbid, should happen, then there's a difficulty.

The nearest hospital is in a town called Nenagh in Co Tipperary. It is a typical Irish county hospital serving the surrounding countryside well over very many years. Now however, the mandarins responsible for mangling our health service have decreed that meaningful activity should cease in such hospitals, piously evoking patient safety as the cause. "Centres of excellence" were to be established in the general vicinity to accommodate patients displaced from downgraded local hospitals. It all sounded very logical.

Solemn undertakings were given that no diminution of the existing service would take place until the replacement facilities were in place both regarding the number of beds and the services required to get the patients to this paragon hospital and also to care for them in the community after discharge.
They lied of course and the new beds and facilities are not in place. They are promised for the end of 2010 or 2011 or whenever. Given the state of our economy, 2050 is just possible. You couldn't put off your visit for a while or

maybe bring your own hospital?

Remember Barack at the beginning of the letter I said we were doing fine here? Well, I lied too and if by any chance you had a few billion dollars lying handy, you might bring them along.

Wishing you success in the new job and sorry for the béal bocht bit at the end.

I remain yours in friendship,
Muiris

January 27th, 2009

Selecting our future doctors

The great physician and teacher Sir William Osler is reputed to have said to his colleague William Welch in John Hopkins Hospital in Baltimore: "Welch, it is lucky that we got in as professors, we could never enter as students." Criteria for medical school entry change over the years. In my time you had to have the Leaving Certificate which had to include Latin, Maths and English. Oh, and your parents had to pay the fees.

Free third-level education removed that stipulation but with the passage of years the academic requirements steadily increased. In the purely Irish setting, the points required to do medicine became almost stratospheric for those wishing to join the profession.

Unfortunately, the all-pervading necessity to obtain the required points began to obscure the vocational aspects of a doctor's life. You do not need a plethora of points to be a good doctor. You do need to really want to be a doctor. The multiplicity of points showed that you were clever and capable of application and hard work. That's all it meant and for those whose heart and soul wanted to study medicine, it was more than enough. It opened the door also to some who simply did medicine because they had the required scores and had no real feeling for the subject.

The same Sir William Osler used to tell his students annually; "We are here to add what we can to life, not to get what we can from life." So how do we select those of reasonable and appropriate academic standard who have also a genuine calling to be a doctor?

All sorts of suggestions have been made over the years including indepth interviews, work experience in a medical field, and that points harvesting should be restricted to core subjects having medical application like maths, physics, chemistry, biology, English and possibly Latin. The rationale for this is simply that in this era, medicine is a complex scientific subject. I am not sure that in these days, when graduate entry to medical school is a fact, that a primary degree that does not encompass a scientific background is a good preparation for the study of medicine.

Now, for the time being at least, the requirements for undergraduate entry to medical school have been set at 480 points in the Leaving Certificate plus a satisfactory score in the Health Professionals Admissions Test or HPat. This is a multi-faceted aptitude test and is similar to UMAT, the Australian model and is administered by the same group; ACER.

It consists of a two-and-a-half hour paper with three sections. Firstly, there is logical reasoning and problem solving. The second is labelled as interpersonal understanding. The third section is described as non-verbal reasoning. The test has a multiple choice format. It is held only once a year in several centres in the State. I have serious reservations about this latter point as several compelling reasons could prevent a student presenting on the given day.

Otherwise, it all sounds very logical and has drawn favourable comments from the medical schools on its first year of operation. It appears, however, that a certain amount of tuition would be required to allow a candidate approach the test with any prospect of success. I looked at the sample questions and I feel many who had qualified before would have some difficulty attuning to this examination. So the students would have to be taught and since this is not a formal subject, the teaching may attract people giving grinds on how to pass the test.

This is not necessarily a bad thing, since the questions and problems are capable of almost infinite variation and thus not amenable to rote learning or cramming. However, books of questions will appear and claims of institutions achieving x% success in the exam. It is hard to see a way around this and it is said to have achieved consistent and fair results in Australia and in the UK medical schools. If it lessens the proportion of square pegs in round holes, it will be an advance.

Such selections are incapable of certainty and one can readily imagine a sense of grievance in some students who might have obtained very high marks in the old regime, but who performed poorly in the HPat and, accordingly, missed a place in medical school. They may well have made fine doctors.

Early observations on its first year in existence would indicate that it has gone some way towards adjusting the gender balance among medical students. In earlier years the profession was predominantly male. In recent times the split has been 70-30 in favour of female students. Now it has come back to 50-50.

It would appear that the lads might be better at solving the problems posed. We shall see. Personally I am reluctant to enter that particular minefield. Irrespective of gender, we need caring committed doctors who perform to the best of their ability. This is the first step and it appears a reasonable way to select our future doctors.

I will leave the last word to Osler. "The hardest conviction to get into the mind of a beginner is that the education upon which he is engaged is not a college course, nor a medical course, but a life course, for which the work of a few years under teachers is but a preparation."

August 25th, 2009

I was wrong about the children's hospital site

I spent my consultant cardiac surgical career between the Mater Hospital in Eccles Street and Our Lady's Hospital for Sick Children, Crumlin (OLHC). The round trip from my home was about 16 miles and the journey became more onerous as the city and its population grew. When the Mater was selected as the site for the National Paediatric Hospital in 2006, I welcomed the decision and wrote about it in this column. I also mentioned that the reasons for the selection and the process employed should be open to scrutiny. I could have saved the ink.

The Mater also was my mother hospital and was and is a very fine institution. The HA and three of our children worked there. Sara had all her working life there before she left long before her time. I was happy that it had secured this prestigious development. It would have been very convenient for us cardiac surgeons and the paramedical perfusion personnel who then worked from both locations.

I was asked recently to review my stance on the project. I did so, and in all honesty I think my original position was wrong. I had unwittingly passed over many little problems. This wasn't about me, or the convenience of my colleagues or prestigious and academic considerations. It was about the "little problems", the sick children and what was best for them. I feel that neither the Mater nor the joint children's hospitals may be best served by this proposed development on a geographically constrained site.

Staffs from the various hospitals to be amalgamated were gathered together recently to be briefed on the current status of the project and to be told the planning schedule for enabling works and final planning permission. They were shown an impressive site model including the iconic tower of the children's hospital, which would dominate the area. They were told that 1,000 parking spaces would be provided underground. It was to be the paediatric Promised Land.

Given our present economic circumstances, this project is not about totemic architecture, however excellent. It is about sick children and their families.

The Minister for Health warns us that there are to be severe cuts in the health budget. Such cuts will further diminish services to those with no recourse other than to the dysfunctional public system. At the same time we are given to understand that the National Paediatric Hospital with its ring-fenced monies of at least €500 million is to move forward at speed. OLHC has endured ward and theatre closures and lengthening waiting lists for years past. In what way would relocation improve this situation, since many of its problems have their origins in inadequate staffing levels? A much more modest investment on its current site and agreed staffing levels would hold the fort until the sun shines again.

I am surrounded by reams of documents and I am analysing dubious claims such as that hoary old chestnut "best practice", which can be made to fit a variety of conflicting views. One of the dubious claims here is that the National Children's Hospital should be in association with an adult teaching hospital. It is not specified why this should be the case.

Indeed, one of the experts consulted by the Task Force told us that he was not consulted on location and added that Dublin's three children's hospitals together are large enough to stand alone. Prof Alan Craft, past president of the Royal College of Paediatrics, said his "extensive consultation" had been a telephone conversation with a member of the Task Force. He had not seen its report nor was he involved in making the decision about the site. It all sounds wearyingly familiar. Crucial decisions were made on limited and selective criteria and without honest debate among those most qualified at home to give advice, and driven by concerns far beyond the welfare of the children.

John Betjeman wrote in 'First and Last Loves': "Oh prams on concrete balconies, what will your children see." We can do better, and in view of the fact this National Children's Hospital is about all the sick children of Ireland, not just Dublin, let's look for a greenfield site, spacious and easy of access. In these days of Nama and sequestered land banks, such may be available.

A radical thought suggests itself. How about making the nation's children the template for universal health insurance and devolve to interested parties the building and running of the facility subject to stringent safeguards?

July 27th, 2010

One health vision that must become a reality

I was not cut out to be a psychiatrist. The surgical vocation requires clearer diagnoses and treatment pathways in so far as are possible. My early and indeed woefully short exposure to psychiatry was the mandated course before we faced final medical exams. This consisted of a series of lectures and visits to a clinical setting. In my case this was to Grangegorman, which later became St Brendan's Hospital.

I have always had the impression that changing the name of a hospital is often an attempt to leave negative connotations behind. In my time, psychiatry was a Cinderella specialty, overshadowed by the cutting edge disciplines of medicine and surgery. I learned enough of the subject to pass my exams, but I now think far more tuition and experience would have stood me in good stead in later practice.

There was a tendency to quickly refer such patients to the appropriate colleague lest the order of your practice was dislocated and your beds occupied by problems deeper than those cured by the knife. Walter Lincoln Palmer, distinguished physician, adjured colleagues, "Don't send a patient to a psychiatrist as if you were telling him to go to hell." There was, and to some degree remains, an "out of sight, out of mind" approach to such patients. The medical student's superficial conclusion that the subject concerned the "care of the id by the odd" was not conducive to considering the very real issues involved.

In medicine, luckily, there are always bigger and better minds than your own. The great pioneering surgeon John Hunter wrote, "Perhaps there is nothing in nature more pleasing than the study of the human mind." More tellingly, the equally distinguished physician Sir William Osler, in his classic 'Principles and Practice of Medicine', said, "Everywhere the old order changes and happy they are who can change with it." There was a lot to change in the treatment of those with diseases of the mind; there remains a lot to improve.

It has been a long and arduous road to the incorporation of psychiatry fully into the body of mainstream medicine. Such illnesses are like most others – a mixture of genetic, social, biological and psychological functions. The genesis of many psychiatric conditions is as yet poorly understood, but we must ensure that the treatment of those with such conditions is not allowed to be dealt with once more on the "out of sight, out of mind principle". Society has for too long turned its back on these patients.

In earlier days, some patients with epilepsy and other neurological and psychiatric conditions were associated with demonic possession and witchcraft, and many perished cruelly because of our fears of the unknown. Others were banished from society or incarcerated so that the rest of us could remain secure in our ignorance.

The Bethlehem or Bedlam Hospital established in London in 1330 is a case in point. There were held a mixture of the "mentally disabled, the criminally insane, epileptics and indigent poor" and one might be tempted to add "other inconvenient persons".

The Pitié-Salpêtrière Hospital in Paris served the same function and also was a prison for the flotsam and jetsam of the lower classes. It was stormed during the French Revolution and while incarcerated prostitutes were freed by the mob, many shackled "lunatics" were murdered in cold blood. With the dawn of enlightenment, this great hospital grew into the world class institution it is today.

Pierre Janet, writing about the Paris of the time, pointed out the class distinctions of psychiatric practice: "If a patient is poor, he is committed to a public hospital as 'psychotic', if he can afford the luxury of a private sanatorium, he is diagnosed as 'neurasthenic', if he can afford to be nursed at home with attending physicians, the diagnosis is 'eccentric'. In some respects, plus ça change.

In our little island, the great Dean Swift wrote of his own death:

He gave the little wealth he had
To build a house for fools and mad,
And showed by one satiric touch
No nation needed it so much

Now we talk the talk with our Vision for Change document for the mental health services here. Will we walk the walk, or will these vulnerable patients be sacrificed with so many more of our people for the failures of others?

This was Maurice Neligan's last column for The Irish Times,
published four days after he died, on October 12th, 2010

FAMILY & LEISURE

Having a good puck

I have not placed my sanity at risk over the past few weeks by meditating on the vagaries of the health service. Instead, I have opted for a sojourn in the real world. I am writing this on a windless day with a flat calm sea, and the smoke from the houses opposite on the lower slopes of Seefin rising vertically in the still air. This, I believe, ranks as zero on the Beaufort scale of wind velocity.

The weather mattered little in my full-time working days. Now, however, it assumes much greater significance. This is because so much time is spent outdoors, and wind, tides, rainfall and temperature become very important. The mysteries of weather forecasting remain obscure to an amateur like myself but in this little haven of Dooks, Co Kerry, thankfully the more dire predictions often prove unfounded. This has been a summer for the active type, rather than the beach potato, and that suits me fine.

I have frequently been asked if I miss surgery and the everyday activity, bustle and undoubted challenge of hospital life. I must answer truthfully, I do not. As I continue to chronicle my passage through a medical lifetime, I shall endeavour to explain this. Over-administration, pointless time-consuming paperwork, diversion of resources into the shadow rather than the substance of healthcare, and lack of sensible and coherent policy are a few of the reasons I and many of my colleagues feel relief at the end of active participation in an endless struggle.

That being said, most remain deeply committed to change, although now working from without. I note that we are to have an aptitude test for entry to medical school and, possibly, also for nursing school. In the latter instance, it might be asked why 70 per cent of our graduating nurses have left the profession within 18 months of graduation. It is very important that we examine such proposals very carefully indeed, lest we open a Pandora's box containing the seeds of destruction for what is left of the caring professions.

These latter proposals come through the Department of Education. There is no point in lining up the usual parrots to regurgitate the current theory, which is usually a mixture of political correctness and arrant nonsense. Without listening to the voices of working - and I stress the word working - doctors and nurses, no worthwhile progress will be made.

Back to the real world. Where I am now is seven miles from Killorglin and we are in the post-Puck period. I suppose everybody knows about Puck Fair, and certainly I am not competent to write its history. Simply, it is a three-day celebration, homecoming, cattle and horse fair and exuberant festival. Held on the 10th, 11th, 12th of August and of uncertain origins lost in antiquity, it is an epochal event here and one by which time is measured. It is, together with the Auld Lammas fair in Ballycastle, and the horse fair in Ballinasloe, one of Ireland's great fairs.

We do know that James I gave a patent to Jenkins Conway "to hold a a faire Killorgan on Lammas Day and the day after". This was given in 1613 and the fair existed long before that date. There is a tradition that at the hiring fairs in Killorglin in February a stipulation of those hired was that they had three days holiday for Puck. More cynically, it was suggested that the servant girls hired were promised three days for Puck and a child for Christmas.

In 'Rambles in Ireland' (1912), Robert Lynd describes a banner, with "Eire gan

Meisce, Eire gan Spleadachas" (Ireland sober, Ireland free) on it, strung across the square in Killorglin. A more inappropriate placement cannot be imagined. If you have not been to Puck, come and see for yourselves what a wonderful occasion it is, "where the goat acts the king and the people act the goat". Enter into the spirit of the event and enjoy yourselves. The pubs are no longer open 24 hours. They close now at 4 am and re-open at 8 am, so thirst could be a problem.

The only serious crime this year was that apparently somebody smoked a cigarette in a pub. An intensive manhunt (personhunt?) is still under way but the culprit is rumoured to have fled to the mountains with the dethroned goat. Come and enjoy a wonderful event amongst lovely people. See you all at the next Puck.

August 31st, 2004

Go slow on the quick fix

Another dire weather prediction may come to pass this afternoon here in the south west. I sincerely hope not, as I am due to play golf. God how I miss work and I envy all you lucky people in whatever working environment, as you prop up the national economy. The fruits of your labour will be wisely used by the Government for the betterment of all, and you may feel justly proud of your contribution. Our cat has just laughed outside the window. I wonder why?

I am mentally preparing to return to the metropolis from my refuge on the Iveragh Peninsula, apparently one of the healthiest places on earth. Charles Smith in Ancient and Present State of the County of Kerry, refers to Mr Daniel MacCarty, who died in 1751 at the age of 112 years, having lived all his life in this barony. He buried four wives and, at the age of 84, married again to a girl of 14 years and who survived him with their several children. He apparently drank great quantities of rum, but also walked eight to 10 miles a day. Mr Smith surmises: "Thus it appears that there is no habitable place, but where some constitutions, especially such as are inured to it, will weather life to an old age, with almost any method of living."

He continues by giving instances of longevity in other climes, amongst both the abstemious and the profligate. This book was published in 1756 and I am sure that if Mr Smith were to revisit us now and read the healthcare section of this newspaper, that he would be very interested. He would find those who advocate only organic foods, or those who adhere to one diet or another, or those who chop up the doormat for use as a breakfast cereal (bulk, you know) all seem to claim that their recipe leads to the amelioration of all worldly woes.

There is a story here about the cub reporter on a local newspaper who plagued the editor for permission to write a feature article. Finally, he directed her to a residence for senior citizens with a brief to interview the oldest men therein and to ascertain the secret of their longevity. On approaching the first old man, he told her that he was 104 years old and that he felt his long life was due to total abstinence, no tobacco, hard work and the fact that he never married.

Impressed, she turned to the second man and repeated the question. His answer was identical: no drink, no smokes, no sex and lots of hard work. He was 94. The last old gentleman looked considerably older, and the enquiry was repeated. "I'm not like them other bucks at all: I drank all my life, never worked a day, smoked at least 40 a day, and chased every woman in the town." And what age are you Sir? "Begod I'm nearly 58," was the reply. I think Mr Smith would have understood that. In passing, it is noteworthy that amongst the ranks of the senior citizens, the ladies far outnumber the men.

There are sound medical reasons for this, and you must disabuse yourselves of notions that the women do less work, or that the men are nagged underground earlier. Such thoughts would be unworthy and certainly not politically correct. The amount of medical information in Mr Smith's book is remarkable. Chapter 11 is devoted to the medicinal waters of Kerry and their analysis. Some of the claims for their efficacy would sit well in the present time.

Dr William Collis observed one spring that an earthworm placed in its waters soon died! Drunk in quantities of three pints to two quarts, it had a diuretic effect. Using more than this could be purgative, and really hogging it could be emetic.

From my student days, I had thought that these were properties of beer, and had I known of the above, I could have told my late mother that I was suffering from a bad glass of water. This remarkable water cured jaundice and disposition to dropsy. It also cured tabid habits - whatever they are. It helped in numerous other conditions. I don't know where to acquire this elixir now, but if I ever find it I am sure I need never work again. All this means little has changed in 250 years. We are still looking for the quick-fix to the problems of health. The reality is painstakingly slow research and development by those trained to do it, not the latest scatterbrained fad.

I suppose I become more tolerant as I grow older.

September 7th, 2004

A year in writing

It is just one year since I exchanged the scalpel for the pen. That sounds very pompous and what I really mean is that I have been writing these articles in The Irish Times for a year now. This came about following a phone call from Dr Muiris Houston, initially received by my wife. On the day in question I had been proffering advice on the organisation and running of the household. As in retirement I had lots of time and I felt that on my golf-free days my involvement in the domestic scene would be most helpful. This was particularly so as I remembered that any domiciliary disturbance during my working years was invariably accompanied by cries of "you're never here" or worse, "what would you know about it".

Now I had lots of time and enthusiasm yet somehow my heartfelt offers of involvement were met with a kind of polite evasion. Similarly on the day in question, I had given my two youngest daughters a "money doesn't grow on trees" type of exhortation. This involved simple things like turning off lights, radios, fires, etc. En passant, I gave them my experiences of studying, intended as some practical help. I gained the strong impression that all of this was not regarded kindly or felt to be in the least helpful. Both hurriedly disappeared, leaving the paternal advice unfinished and indeed in the fullness of time, unheeded.

It was at this stage that my wife told me about the call from Muiris and mentioned that it had something to do with writing an article. She added a wholly unnecessary observation that it would give me something useful to do with my time. Even I, obtuse as I sometimes can be, realised that my well-meaning intentions of domestic involvement were greeted with consternation, indeed horror. I had, however, been willing to give it a try. Thus rebuffed on the domestic and parental scenes I returned the call to Muiris. He succinctly explained about the Health Supplement and how they would welcome an article on a weekly basis.

There were to be no hard and fast rules about content but I presumed that it should be in some way tangential to medicine. It was to be about 850 words and, sting in the tail, it was to be submitted electronically. My pleas of computer illiteracy fell on deaf ears and it was implied that if I got off my arse, I could learn quite quickly. In the face of total determination on the home front that this would come to pass, I became a part-time journalist.

I now faced the problem of content. What was to be the subject matter? I did not want merely to be a critic of the health service, indeed I could contribute several volumes of such criticism but as Pope expressed: "All seems infected that th'infected spy, As all looks yellow to the jaundiced eye." Accordingly, I settled for a melange of experience, criticism and reminiscence. This allows me wander among the issues of the day and engage in fantasy, speculation and above all memory.

Sadly, the articles did not write themselves and a certain amount of discipline became necessary, reminiscent of finishing the homework in the distant past. I had ambitions of having three or four articles written in advance, but the world, particularly the medical world, kept changing and frustrated this simple ambition.

The freedom to write and express your views is not enjoyed by many people.

Listening to colleagues in the medical and nursing professions, it is abundantly clear that this is the case. There is an attempt to stifle patient advocacy by the caring professions and to spin a web of deceit at great expense, to pretend that things are better than they are. I receive communications from all over the country portraying the true sorry situation. Sadly the authors cannot speak publicly for fear of victimisation. This is no idle fear.

The freedom to write is the freedom of advocacy. To think about and articulate to the best of your ability the problems of the day, realising that these go far beyond the travails of the health service. I feel as do many that the prosperity of the past few years has been dissipated in show and not in substance. If the bad times come, have we made prudent provision? I fear not and I hope I am proved wrong.

Finally on a personal level, I have been writing now for a year. I ought to be entitled to a raise under the terms of "The Programme for Posturing and Penury" or whatever the current scheme to perpetuate the Government in office is fancifully called. This is all sanctioned by the unholy Trinity (The Social Partners). It does not seem to matter whether the country can afford it or not. I would like to be benchmarked and secure my seat on the gravy train, before the real world rudely intrudes.

February 1st, 2005

Nostalgia: not what it was

Whatever happened to you my friend, whatever happened to me,
what became of the people we used to be?
(The Likely Lads)

Several things contributed to this outburst of nostalgia. I recently attended a 50th anniversary reunion of my leaving year class from Blackrock College. Approximately half of our 110-strong class attended, many having travelled long distances to do so. Twenty-three of our classmates are dead and we were unable to contact another 20, some of whom may have also passed on.

Amidst the celebrations and the routine viewing of the past through highly selective retrospection, this was a sobering thought. We are now, like it or not, in the firing line; He is picking them out of our barrel now. It is probably best dealt with by simply not entertaining it. It is not merely, as William Dunbar put it 500 years ago, a matter of *Timor mortis conturbat me*.

Amidst the rejoicing there was some sadness and realisation of the ephemeral nature of things. We had won the Leinster Schools' Senior Cup that year of 1955, part of five in a row, and as I recollect we didn't even have a sports psychologist. There were happy and good things to remember among us, many of whom had not met in the intervening period. It was humbling to pray together and dine together in the place where we had been so happy and carefree and to compare the passage of our lives.

This is a grey afternoon in Holy Week and it has been raining steadily for several hours. The clouds envelop uplands of the hills and mountains and wreaths of mist explore the valleys. The landscape and the seascape cover all shades of grey. It is extraordinarily quiet here in Dooks, Co Kerry, compared to Dublin. In truth it is quiet compared to anywhere else. If you go past our house, you go into the water as we are the last habitation on this little road.

Upon our arrival here the other day as I opened up the house as usual I was taken aback and almost overpowered by the feeling of things past. This was triggered by the stillness and by walking through the children's rooms. There was total quiet and order everywhere, the only occupant being Paddington Bear who sat forlornly on one of the beds in the girls' room. The contrast with the chaos, noise and sheer exuberance of former years was overwhelming. Our children had magic summers and holidays here, and formed firm friendships still strong today. The magic of this wonderful place enveloped them as it had their parents and without exception they love to return.

There were never enough hours then to accomplish what must be done - swimming, boating, golf, hill walking and so on. The weather was always perfect and the hours passed more quickly here than anywhere else. The time passed too quickly and the young grew up. To the above-mentioned wholesome pursuits was added the capacity for indulging in mayhem and enjoying same. Late nights, ignored when possible by parents, late breakfasts, often with waves of previously unseen humanity, became the rule. I even suspect that some of my children may have had a drink. I am conscious that this was an unworthy suspicion but I suspect that many parents may have shared it.

The idyllic periods were interrupted by the harsh intrusions of the real world. School and examinations, college and examinations, pressed forward relentlessly.

Then came the awful realisation that the long summers, Easters, Christmases were things of the past. Ironically they existed now for the parents whose sojourns in Hy Brasil became more frequent.

All our young adults come back whenever they can and at times it is almost as if they never left. It is however rare now to have them all together and we miss that. At least we tell each other that we do. They take up a lot more room now and although disguising it well they feel they should be nice to the two old fossils who pass for parents. Easter approaches and we wish they were all here. There is a bright side. We save on eggs.

Recently I heard some excuse being made for a toddling grandson on the basis that he was in the period known as the terrible twos. We are all familiar with tweens and teenagers and their special problems. On the male parental side of this equation I am beginning to be oppressed by the notion that in fact children can be expected to be at their worst between 40 and 50. This feeling that we ain't seen nothing yet is, I am sure, unduly pessimistic and our lot still have some time to prove me wrong.

On arrival here on this occasion it was pointed out to me that several disturbing portents had been noted, the meaning of which was unclear. A blue moon had been noted on the 17th and again on the 20th and pigs had been seen to fly around it. The meaning of these omens was unclear. On consulting Nostradamus I think they alluded to the fact that an obscure Dublin school had won the Leinster Schools' rugby double and that such frightening manifestations were unlikely to recur. Hence the saying "once in a blue moon". Nostradamus also mentioned that this school had produced a brilliant rugby-playing athlete called O'Reilly, and some fellow called Joyce who wrote arcane books. I realised with a start that I had some friends who had actually attended this place, including my best man. I would like to reassure them that their secret is safe with me.

March 29th, 2005

Looking after elderly in all our interest

Rose early, that is early in my present life, around 7am. The sun was shining and the sky was almost clear. It was full tide and the water was flat calm, mirroring the hills and the occasional passing cloud. The grass in the meadow was unruffled and a cock pheasant poked unhurriedly around the margins. A disorderly mob of siskins, greenfinches and chaffinches pushed and jostled at the bird table and feeders. The earliest swallows were abroad and our robin in residence worked the ground under the feeders. Rabbits abounded on the drive and in the meadow. It was a genuinely "good to be alive" morning with the promise of a nice day.

I am ashamed to say that my purpose in being abroad at this early hour was not to enjoy the beauties of nature. Rather I was about to transform myself into a couch potato for the next two hours while I watched the Lions play Taranaki. I am further ashamed to say that this necessitated drawing the blinds thus excluding the wonderful world of light outside. But there you are; we all have our secret vices. Solitary peace for the next two hours and I was free to advise the referee without the disapproval of my sons, all of whom know much more about rugby than I do. Come to think of it, they know much more about everything than I do.

The Lord of the Rings and now the Lions tour revive my interest in returning to New Zealand which I had only briefly visited before. I did not feel at all guilty as I returned to the real world. I had, however, to solve some major problems. Would I have a swim? Maybe this evening when the tide would have come in over the warm sand. Would I play golf? No, not after the catastrophes of the previous few days, this caused God and I to be no longer on speaking terms. I will have to sneak up unannounced on golf and take it by surprise. How then do I get my moderate exercise?

I was presented recently with a pedometer by my good wife. The ostensible purpose was to record my mileage or lack of same during the day but I harbour the suspicion that she really wanted me out from under her feet. I was told that the basic requirement just to stay alive was approximately 7,000 steps (3.5 miles) per day and that if you wanted to be more ambitious than that, eg to get slightly fit, you needed 10,000 steps. It is a simple inexpensive device and has proved reasonably accurate. There are deluxe models which give information about calories and things but such are really only for true believers. Trouble is the bloody thing is making me obsessive. Late at night I look at the display, 9,719 steps. Off I go again around the garden or the house and lo! 10411 steps. Goal attained. Then I press the button to translate into miles, 5.81, well, clearly you want to even this up to six miles, so off again.

I can now identify and measure various walks in Dublin and Kerry to fit the shortfalls. If anybody should see me walking about aimlessly at night, they will now know that I have a hidden agenda. On golf days I have no trouble with numbers - 15,000 to 20,000 steps being common achievements. I should point out that my golf and that of my usual partners would not be exactly tee to green and a certain amount of exploring or indeed orienteering is customarily part of the game. Other days you may have to make a big effort, particularly in bad weather or more often when you are simply feeling lazy. Nonetheless it has changed my attitude, stairs instead of lifts, walk to shops, etc. This can only be good and I am already entertaining the delusion that I am feeling fitter.

Sloth is appealing and pernicious and so it is very important to keep muscles and joints exercised when possible and thus prolong active life. Sleep and appetite are beneficiaries and more importantly so is peace of mind. Get up you fat slobs and start moving. If I can do it, anybody can. This is of course age-related. I am talking of activity levels that many people of my generation aspire to, not those gaunt figures that inhabit gymnasiums and run real marathons. I would be more comfortable with the mini-marathon group progressing gently around Dublin raising money for some worthy cause. Exercise is clearly good for you and common sense and peer group example are your best guides as to how much. This isn't about living forever, but it is about retaining your mobility and with it, hopefully, your independence for as long as possible.

The Prime Time programme on RTÉ recently drew everybody's attention to the problem areas of caring for the elderly in our society. I think many knew there was a problem but sadly it always seems to be somebody else's problem. At least acknowledging that a problem exists is the first step to fixing it. Like all health issues it is complex and not amenable to "one size fits all" solutions. We are dealing with different groups of people with different needs, the wholly well, those with physical restraints, those with psychiatric illness and those with dementia. These groups all pose different problems and require different levels of care and nursing. Clearly in some instances they have not been cared for correctly to state it at its least offensive.

As usual our dysfunctional health service was found wanting. The prattle about the public-private mix had again been found wanting and I personally feel it has little to offer in the delivery of health which must be dedicated to the patient and not to the pursuit of profit. An awful lot of us are going to live to the age where we may require such services and if it is only for self interest, let the service not be found wanting. I hope we care for more altruistic reasons.

June 14th, 2005

A rocky oasis

Laurence Sterne wrote that "men tire themselves in pursuit of rest". This is a conundrum of retirement. The longed for, dreamed of days of calm and quiet never seem to materialise. There is never enough time for everything you want to do; there is never enough time for all the books you had intended reading. Some time ago, I promised my sister and brother-in-law that when they visited us in Kerry this summer, I would take them out to Skellig Michael. This seemed a good idea at the time, discussed in a relaxed atmosphere with good food and wine. These kinds of airy promises have a way of presenting themselves for fulfilment and, accordingly, I found myself in Portmagee last Sunday morning awaiting Eoin Walsh's boat, the *Aengus Olibhear*, which was to bear us out to the islands.

The boat duly arrived and we were handed down into same. At this stage I had my first faint premonition that I was not as lithe as heretofore and that memories of a trip of some years before might well have been softened by the passage of time. It was a lovely morning with only a light breeze, and our small group of tourists/pilgrims settled down happily for the voyage. I remarked hopefully to our skipper, Eoin, that it seemed calm enough. He replied enigmatically that it would be choppy enough beyond "the heads". He was right of course, and facing into the wind and tide we set sail on our nine-mile journey. We passed Bray Head on our right (I mean starboard) and on our port side we passed the three Death Rocks, a piece of information that I did not share with my travelling companions.

Bolus Head was cleared to the south and then Puffin Island. Wrapped in oilskins, we took stock of our surroundings. Looking back, there was a magnificent receding view of the Kerry coastline and dead ahead the Skelligs slowly grew on the horizon. The first gannets appeared, swooping low over the waves, and occasionally a sail was glimpsed in the distance. The only characteristic I may share with the Ancient Mariner might be the ability to bore you all, but I must confess that the rolling sea is not my preferred environment. The medical consequence of the choppy condition soon affected our little group despite exhortations to fix eyes firmly on the horizon and not to move your head.

The gannets became more numerous and our first puffins were seen riding the swell with considerably more aplomb than ourselves. We passed under the lee of the Little Skellig, which was wall-to-wall gannets, and duly noted a few disinterested seals lounging on the rocks at the base of the cliffs. Finally, we crossed the stretch of water between the islands, heading for our landing at Blind Man's Cove. For what can be a very difficult landing, ours was totally uncomplicated and thus we were marooned for 2½ hours.

Now it was that memory and reality really clashed. I remembered a gentle stroll up the 600 or so steps to the monastery. Reality, and the realisation that I was probably the oldest person on the island, told me that I should have more sense than to be here at all. Pride stirred and I banished such thoughts and set off for the top. As I proceeded, I became acutely conscious of the passage of years. Hips, knees, balance and cardiovascular system were rigorously examined. Incongruously, I was reminded of Marilyn Monroe's remark when chided for being rude to the late Harold Macmillan, then prime minister of the UK: "who dat guy, dat old stumblebum?" I was that soldier.

I reached the middle of the climb at the area known as Christ's Saddle, rested briefly and for the first time looked down. That was not a good idea. Then I set off again on a very steep section of the path that was devoid of handholds on either side. I was proceeding slowly upwards, like some form of demented crab, when disaster struck: I wrenched my back. My heroic struggle to reach the top would require another volume, but eventually sanctuary was achieved in this wondrous place.

I wondered like everybody else at the motivation of the monks who had established their monastery on this isolated rock, 600 ft above sea level. How they built it, how they subsisted, how long they lived; all these questions presented themselves.

> *Cells that freeze*
> *The thin pale monks upon their knees*
> *Bodies worn with rites austere*
> *The falling tear - Heaven's King loves these.*
> (Flower, from the Gaelic)

Not only is the monastery an oasis of calm and peace, but on the other peak of the island a hermitage was constructed 700 ft sheer above the sea. The path to this is no longer accessible to the public, but was once a well-known penitential pathway. It required a firm nerve and a head for heights. When the penitent reached the summit, he or she edged out astride a pinnacle of rock known as "the spit" and kissed the cross at its extremity. On either side there was a vertical drop to the sea. They were some men, these monks.

> *Melodious bell*
> *That is struck in a night of wind*
> *I had rather make tryst with it*
> *Than with wanton womankind.*
> (Carney, from the Gaelic)

Maybe there is another clue there. The lads were chased out - anything for a quiet life. If you have not been to Skellig Michael, come here and feel the power and spirituality of this holy place. It will more than repay the effort.

August 1st, 2006

A very weighty issue

I went to the Ryder Cup. For me it was a marvellous occasion. Everybody involved is worthy of the highest commendation. As we all know now, the only adverse feature was the weather. But the Government has promised it will see to that after the next general election and will ensure it can never recur.

From Dr Michael Smurfit's ambitious dream to its hugely successful implementation, there were years of hard work, dedication, talent and commitment. We the public, the golfers and even those weird people who don't like golf were the beneficiaries. So was Ireland in the widest sense. There were, of course, begrudgers and to them I can only proffer the time-honoured Irish salutation. The less well-bred among you will immediately recognise this.

The Highest Authority and I were there on the final day and we had a ball. In every way it was a day to savour and remember. From the amenity garden at the entrance displaying the Ryder Cup, to the food island in the lake with its 11,000 heathers and grasses, everything illustrated the richness and diversity of the Irish food industry.

As a nation, we have become more appreciative in our enjoyment of good food. In an earlier existence, I unwittingly wandered into the food faddist's den and was savagely mauled. In fact, I was accused of misleading the public, essentially over the margarine versus butter issue. I had the temerity to urge the widespread use and enjoyment of our incomparable dairy products. However, that is all in the past and science forges steadily forward, bypassing the islands of single-issue fanatics who would impede its progress.

Personally, I don't worry too much about what people eat. Commonsense dictates to most of us what we should eat and education provides a basic understanding of nutrition. Alas, this latter can often prove to be indigestible to the recipient. My simple and wholly fallible creed consists of moderation in all things (including moderation), a varied diet and lots of exercise. If you choose to believe that following a particular diet and/or exercise regime is somehow beneficial, that is your prerogative. I would venture to suggest however that the weight of human experience does not illuminate such a pathway and people of all races and nations tend to muddle on in their own way with the eventual outcome being the same.

My own inclination would be to face the challenges nutritionally posed by want rather than affluence. I actually do find it hard to work up indignation over a hamburger or two; while widespread starvation shames us all. I had not intended to write about this subject at all, but for the fact that upon return from the K Club with its culinary delights and lavish hospitality, the Highest Authority made the statement: "I think you've put on weight." There was no "you might have". This was definite. I was indignant, and feebly protested that I did not feel fat and that I knew my weight had not changed. Nonetheless, I surreptitiously weighed myself later in the evening.

My first appropriately named gut reaction was that the scale was a lying bastard. My second was that it had just made a simple mistake. I reluctantly admitted to the Highest Authority that I had, in fact, put on an insignificant amount of weight. I resolutely refused to discuss details.

Such matters were to be private between the scales and myself. I thought gloomily back to my consulting room days: the statement, "doctor, he hardly eats anything", would leave you pondering the proposition that a 15-stone man could maintain his weight on two Marietta biscuits a day. I remember being asked for extreme diet sheets, which everyone involved knew would simply end up in the bin. I remembered equally heavy women berating their partners for eating too much. I heard every kind of excuse and vainly pointed out that there were few fat people to be found behind the wire in the concentration camps. Occasionally, the object of correction would retort, "you're not too thin yourself". Such comments I did not deign to notice.

My grudging concession that I had in fact gained some weight empowered the Highest Authority, however. She was in a position to do something about it and now I am striving to keep body and soul together on what amounts to a starvation ration. She maintains that most people would think it normal. I could, of course, supplement my intake outside, but my cunning strategy is to make discernible improvement and then monitor same on a weekly basis. No formal diet; this has to be for me a triumph of mind over matter and of will over want. Hippocrates said: "It is easier to fill up with drink than with food." Don't I know it; there are a lot of calories in a pint.

A week further on, there was some encouragement from my friend the scales, with whom I am once more on speaking terms. In this week I have managed to lose 8lbs. I suspect that this is the easy bit and that things will become harder. This is where the "including moderation" bit comes in my philosophy. I am not a saint in this regard and am looking forward already to a good fall. Thomas Jefferson wrote: "We never repent of having eaten too little." What a load of nonsense some people write.

Watch this space, it may shrink.

October 3rd, 2006

Meet again in sunlit uplands

In an appreciation I wrote about a recently departed colleague, I quoted from American poet Emily Dickinson's poem titled 'The bustle in a house'.

> *The bustle in a house,*
> *The morning after death*
> *Is solemnest of industries,*
> *Enacted upon Earth.*

I know. As many of the readers will know a very bad thing has happened to our family. We have lost our middle child, our beloved daughter Sara, in tragic circumstances. For obvious reasons I am constrained from writing too much about this now.

Dear Sara, I do want to write to you and about you, but as now my heart is too heavy and my eyes too full of tears. Your passing leaves a void in our hearts, which the most loving memories can fill only inadequately. Shelley wrote that "grief itself be mortal". It does not seem so now and we are very far from being so dispassionate. With God's help, the pain will lessen and we will be able to remember you as you were, a beautiful, caring, dignified and compassionate girl and woman who brought so much happiness into so many lives.

Our family has been strengthened and comforted by the truly enormous outpouring of sympathy and succour from friends of all the family, from colleagues, acquaintances, clubs and organisations and from people we never even knew but who reached out their hands to us in our distress. It has been a constant theme in the many thousands of letters we have received that the writers acknowledge that they can but find inadequate words of comfort or indeed no words at all. I would like to say to them all and to those who attended the services for Sara that you provided a strong bulwark for us in our time of sorrow and this family would like to say from our hearts to those who stood with them: God bless you all and thank you.

I am conscious in writing that we are a privileged family with wide-ranging contacts who have rallied to our support. I am aware also that there are many who undergo similar deprivation and indeed worse, who do not have similar support. How they can cope is beyond my comprehension. Yet folk do move on, the strength coming for some from the unquenchable human spirit. For others it comes from faith and the promise of resurrection. We unreservedly believe that we shall meet Sara again in the sunlit uplands.

Returning to contemporary Ireland; much has happened over the past few weeks. We've sort of got a new Government, with a different set of fall guys to replace the PDs who sank almost without trace. Otherwise, it seems, unfortunately, to be the mixture much as before. I do note however that the Minister for Health, Mary Harney, to whom I offer sincere condolences on the death of her mother, has sat down with the consultants to explore the way forward. Hopefully this will issue in an era of consultation and co-operation, rather than antagonism and suspicion.

Col William Blacker (1727-1785), a man solidly of the unionist persuasion on this island, wrote a poem called Oliver's advice. It is a martial work full of fire and does not mince words:

> *He comes the open rebel fierce*
> *He comes the Jesuit sly*
> *But put your trust in God my boys*
> *And keep your powder dry.*

The last line attributed to the Lord Protector, Cromwell himself, is very sage advice indeed. It should be noted carefully by the doctors, nurses and paramedics as they wait to see if anything has really changed. It would be infinitely preferable with goodwill, mutual respect and endeavour to move everything forward together. It would be wearying indeed for our health professionals to mount the barricades once again.

In the past few weeks for obvious reasons I have talked to hundreds of those in the front line of the health service, and I must confess I am not too sanguine about ultimate outcomes. The experience of the past few years has left deep cynicism in its wake but also a powerful sense of solidarity. Having quoted from the Orange side of the Irish equation let me quote from the Green:

> *That hour of weak delusions past*
> *The empty dream has flown*
> *Our hope and strength, we find at last*
> *Is in ourselves, alone*
> (John O'Hagan - 1847)

In plain English, nobody can fix the health service without the willing participation of those working within.

I had alluded to the purchase of the Mater Private for the astronomical sum of €350 million. I read today that the money was advanced by one of our major banks. That is where the health service is headed; profit, not patients, being the motive. Co-location has nothing to do with patient welfare but is merely another prop from an overdeveloped and soon-to-be-troubled construction industry.

Sara, love, when I went through your papers and saw your miserable pay cheques as a fully qualified intensive care nurse, I made a promise to you that your old dad would fight this cynical inequality developing in our society. So I shall. Back to Emily Dickinson and the lines I have quoted before: for us in family for us remains,

> *The sweeping of the Heart*
> *And putting love away*
> *We shall not want to use again*
> *Until eternity.*

July 10th, 2007

Putting up with danger

P G Wodehouse in his introduction to the omnibus edition of his golf stories candidly admits "I was never much of a golfer". Neither am I. The golf courses of Ireland have become very crowded over the past week and Padraig Harrington is to blame. He ought to have known that his victory would bring folks of all ages and physical conditions into the clubs, with all sorts of consequences. In no other sport is the illusion that it is easy, so quickly dispelled. It dawned upon me early in my career that golfers like surgeons don't happen by accident. They have to work at it, very hard indeed. Everybody knows the great golfers practise exhaustively, knocking countless lumps out of Mother Earth in the process. It's a bit similar with trainee surgeons with countless bits being removed from patients. Well, we all have to learn, don't we?

There is of course a difference. Not everybody can be a surgeon, but everybody, surgeons included, think they can be a golfer. Accordingly in the aftermath of Padraig's famous victory, there sallied forth onto the green fields of Ireland, a motley group, of both sexes, the halt, the lame, the otherwise physically challenged motivated by the conviction, "I can do this". I leave out of this collection the hardened addicts who know the real score. They are the folk who set forth in hope rather than expectation and who know that in golf there are only two kinds of shot, "that'll do" and "f*** it". They include those who pontificate wisely about every golf course and every aspect of the game.

Such high handicappers, modestly including myself, can become very low handicappers, indeed almost scratch golfers upon arrival at the 19th hole and that their prowess may exponentially increase with each hole played thereafter. The Highest Authority assures me that I am one such. Who am I to argue? Rather, I am talking of those who appear after a performance like Padraig's, unwittingly hazarding life and limb not only for themselves but for others. They are viewed benignly by manufacturers and purveyors of golf equipment who reckon they can recognise suckers when they see them.

About the only golfing gimmick I have not yet seen is a golfer's St Christopher medal, with the saint holding a golf club rather than a staff. Such a medal would be apposite as golf courses are dangerous places, a fact all too easily forgotten. The more crowded they are and the less experienced the practitioner, the higher the risk. Golf ball strikes are not uncommon, sometimes with serious consequences. The risks can be lessened by adherence to the etiquette of the game, such as not standing ahead of the player making the shot. Standing behind is usually safe. The wayward ball should be accompanied by the cry of "fore", warning those in the vicinity that they stand in mortal danger and allowing them to cover their heads.

On the other hand, a ball dispatched wildly and threatening those in the immediate vicinity is often accompanied by a strangled cry of "Jesus watch out". The Lord is often called upon in such circumstances. Those in danger from such a flying missile and hearing no warning cry almost invariably seek guidance, "Jesus where did that come from?"

Common sense is not an attribute normally associated with golfers but it would seem elementary to those indulging in this or any other physical pastime that they should be reasonably fit. "That was a great game of golf," said Bing Crosby in 1977 before promptly expiring. There are a substantial number of heart attacks on golf courses, some fatal. Many clubs have their own "coronary hill" and such should be approached with care by those whose fitness or medical history calls for caution. Many clubs have invested in cardiac defibrillators although I have often wondered what use such might be to the unfortunate who drops on the 11th, far from the clubhouse.

It is not solely unfavourable terrain or lack of fitness that can cause such an attack. Look around the club bar. We all know golfers who regard the world as pitted against them when they venture forth. A million irritants can provoke a tantrum; slow play ahead, the state of the greens, the bloody committee or the captain for not doing something or other. Such would have been the Cork golfer who, in response to the introduction of gender equality in his club, was reduced to the apoplectic comment of "we only let them in to make the tae and now they want to take over the club".

I leave aside the ankle, knee, hip and back complaints visited on the occasional golfers and the source of so much revenue for the poor doctors and physiotherapists. It's not me, not that I'm unfit, or that my hand eye co-ordination is awful, or that I can't keep my head still and that I wave about like a sapling in the breeze. If only I had a square headed driver or a belly putter, I'd be invincible. If acquiring the latter please note if it's for a concave or, more likely, a convex belly.

Maybe golf should be banned lest people enjoy it. "It is statute and ordained that in na place of the Realme there be used Fute-ball, Golfe or uther and unprofitable sportes," ordained James IV of Scotland in 1491. Me, I'd rate it as dangerous as passive smoke, bonfires and chewing gum.

July 31st, 2007

A marriage that's minted in heaven

My daughter! O my ducats! O my daughter!
(Merchant of Venice; Act ii sc. 8)

I'm really not like Shylock. At least I don't think I am, but there is something about a wedding that sets the Highest Authority and the Lesser Authorities delving among the ducats as if there was no tomorrow. From this you can reasonably deduce that a Lesser Authority, Lisa, has become a Highest Authority in her own right. That, incidentally, does not remove her ability to reinforce my HA should I, by any chance, be perceived as becoming "difficult".

Sons, however, tend to scatter to the wind when faced with such problems. To return to the main theme, I did my duty and warned the unsuspecting groom to be, Dave, in hushed tones and well away from the distaff side of the family, that in Lisa's case the genes ran true from the Highest Authority. The poor fellow seemed to think that was wonderful and sleepwalked his way to his doom. God knows I tried, and now like the rest of us - he's on his own.

Truly there is no more helpless, hapless creature than the Father of the Bride. I had been there before, but time dulls these things and I was jolted back into reality. He has basically only two functions, apart from a brief cameo appearance on the day of the ceremony. First and foremost, he signs the cheques. Secondly he acts as a whipping boy or sin eater, should there be even the slightest wobble in the battle plans.

I shudder to think what would happen if there was a real wobble. Talking of battle plans, these girls would have left Napoleon in the shade. No aspect of the logistics was neglected. His aphorism about marching to the sound of the guns was adjusted to "march to the sound of the ducats". There are survival plans handed down from previous holders of the office. These are obviously unwritten. Who would dare write them down?

The most important is an expansion of the injunction usually given to little children: you should be neither seen nor heard. That is basically true but it does not guard against the inevitable: "Where were you? I've been looking for you for the last three hours!" Escaping to the golf club - or worse still, to the pub - is almost a capital offence, except that the ducat for your bullet in the back of the neck can be better spent. "Do you not care about your daughter's wedding?" You must not ask questions. These are likely to be moronic and, accordingly, not worth answering. Any notion that the question may not have been heard is dispelled by an icy basilisk glare in your direction and by a huddle around the chief protagonist (your little girl), muttering "what's he doing here?" Never proffer advice. In the fraught circumstances of the time when cries of "omiGod" greet even what you perceive to be trifling problems, such advice could have you certified and locked away, only being released for ceremonial purposes on the wedding day.

Above all other precepts and in God's name I warn this. Never question any item of expenditure, however trivial, costly or extravagant you may consider it to be. Don't even think about it. It's like bad thoughts in the old days - don't entertain them. It does not matter if you know that you could obtain the item or service mooted at a tithe of the quoted cost. Bite your lip. The supplier has the ladies in his sights and they are on the charge. The fact that it's your bank balance that is blown away in the heat of battle is irrelevant.

A friend of mine, looking over his shoulder with a haunted look, described the cataclysm that engulfed him when he questioned the price of the bridesmaid's shoes. He compounded this with the remark that the lady in question was far from Cinderella, although he suggested she might be related to her sisters. The final nail was: "Who's going to be looking at her feet anyway?" Torrents of fury and abuse were unleashed upon him and he was only saved, as he was being swept away, by clinging to his cheque book. My sister enquired of me as to whether the Highest Authority would be wearing a hat. My immediate unworthy thought was: "Jesus, how much will that cost?" But then, of course, she'll get lots of wear out of it. Won't she?

I jest, of course. Lisa is a beautiful, talented young lady and marrying a wonderful young man. The Highest Authority and I are intensely proud of her, and so happy for her on her great day. Like all parents we remember her from the beginning and cherish the beautiful memories she gave us. Hopefully there are many more to come.

September 9th, 2008

Going cold turkey
at the racetrack

My turkey racing days are over, but the turkeys running the country still abound. At the close of 2008 and with apologies to the Chinese, what else could you call the year just endured? I suppose I should look back and cover the positive developments in the health service over that time but just now I can't think of any.

While waiting for my memory to function, I will tell you the story of the "racing turkey" as it has vague seasonal connotations. Fado, Fado on a wet, dark late afternoon in the bar of Dooks Golf Club there were only two occupants. I had escaped the domestic chores mandated by the Highest Authority (HA) and was enjoying a reflective pint, and also there was Ger "the Bar". Ger leant over the bar and, while polishing the glasses, enquired if I would like to take a share in a racing turkey. Apparently he knew a likely candidate with a good pedigree and a "giveaway" asking price of only €1,000. We would go halves and share the expenses of training, feeding and entries. I've never been a man for the horses or the dogs but this appealed to me and over my second pint the deal was done.

Periodically, over the months that followed Ger would apprise me of the bird's progress and how it had fared at the tracks all over Kerry. It seemed our investment neither gained nor lost. I tried to ask intelligent questions but I really was a novice and deferred to my partner who was an acknowledged expert on turkey racing. We kept our business to ourselves but curious ears began to pick up the odd fragment of our conspiratorial conversations. Occasionally we were asked outright what we were talking about. We gave nothing away.

Speculation was rife however, as we were clearly talking about a matter of great import and the questions became more persistent. One day I came home to find the Highest Authority, arms akimbo, and clearly displeased. Before I could wish her the time of day she made some remark about a fool and his money being soon parted. I weakly enquired if some financial problem had arisen. I was informed in no uncertain terms that the whole golf club was laughing at me and "that bloody racing turkey". I tried to explain and that it had only cost me €500, which was very good value. This almost triggered apoplexy.

I gathered that she was not in favour of the enterprise and it became an unmentionable subject. For the next few months she explained to her friends that she was married to a gullible half-wit and that, furthermore, there was a long streak of insanity in my family. One of her friends told her that there had been a photograph of Ger and I with the turkey in the Kerryman and this nearly finished her entirely.

All good things come to an end and one day Ger the Bar said to me in the company of others that he thought we should enter the bird in several hurdle races over the autumn. He then blew it by wondering if we could get Mr Bloggs, a diminutive acquaintance as a jockey. The penny finally dropped. In the way of these things, of course, nobody had been fooled for a minute. The straitjacket was put away at home and peace restored. Mind you, it was several years before the Highest Authority could talk dispassionately about turkey racing. I got many miles and great value from that bird and it was a great pity that we had to eat it. In naming the year as that of the Pig it should be noted that the pig only represented the culminating disaster in a year abounding in calamity. There were some credulous people who believed that the "Changing of the Chief Elves" ceremony in mid-year might effect some magical restoration of our fortunes. It didn't, matters got steadily worse. The new Chief Elf and his mates took a long summer holiday to steady the nerves and to calmly assess the direction the economy was taking. The dogs in the street could have told them but we could have told the dogs that they don't listen. They know it all and hence here we are, with paddles in short supply.

Our Chief Elf hasn't been lucky in his generals either. Our lot slept happily while the world exploded all around them and the battlefield was lost. Banks, pigs, pensions, unemployment, medical cards, education - in normal working democracies any one of these would bring clamour for change. Over here the pigs would need to fly before that happened. Well at least the pigs are now in the equation and people are beginning to think that there might be something wrong here. The poor old pigs were bought off the table for a paltry €180 million. Pity we couldn't find €10 million to look after our little girls but then, as these Elves tell us, it's all a matter of priorities.

Happy New Year.

December 30th, 2008

The Kingdom, the power and glory of Sam

I am in fatalistic mood and am putting national and medical problems aside for now. *Fata viam invenient*, wrote Virgil in the 'Aeneid'; so I suppose we can chicken out and leave it to the Fates. Last week I had other things on my mind.

I returned to Kerry on the Friday before the All-Ireland final. Crossing the county boundary at the river Feale it was apparent that the county was on war footing. Green and gold was everywhere. Houses, shops, telegraph poles, schools, were festooned with the Kerry colours. The population was mobilised. This was not any old All-Ireland, God knows Kerry takes them in unbroken stride. This was against the old foe across the border, the Boys of Fair Hill, the Corkmen. Furthermore, they had beaten us in the Munster final and were favourites to avenge their defeat of just two years ago. Raiding parties had already crossed the border and painted red and white graffiti through out the Kingdom, even putting a red jersey and hat on the sacred goat of Killorglin, guarding the crossing of the Laune. Such bravado, indeed arrogance, was intolerable.

Favourites indeed; we'll see about that.

A word of explanation here. My Kerry qualification comes from my paternal grandfather who was Kerry born. The Highest Authority's father was from Ballylongford in North Kerry. By my reckoning that leaves her only about 200 years and me about 400 years before we re-establish ourselves amongst the clans. However, the genes run true and we figure it's well worth the wait. The HA's brother Brian never missed a Kerry match in over 30 years. He attended the semi-final win over Meath and then sadly and suddenly slipped away before the final. We buried him with a Kerry jersey. I trust the Good Lord allowed him attend the final.

The day before the final I played golf on past captains' and presidents' day in Dooks. This, the most scenic golf course in Ireland, was at its very best, bathed in warm sunshine and caressed by a gentle breeze. Nature's omens were auspicious and we assumed it was raining in Cork. At our dinner that evening there was one thing on everybody's mind. This was up close and personal. Kerry were to be led on the morrow by a member of Dooks, Darran O'Sullivan, and three other members of the panel came from the Glenbeigh/ Glencar club or from Cromane, our immediate environs. I polled my companions about the outcome. They were staunch to a man.

Final day was bright and clear. Kerry flags flew in the church grounds in Cromane. Kerry jerseys were everywhere in the congregation. Defeat was not an option. I remembered a late great friend and Kerry footballer Colm Kennelly, then county engineer, big brother to Brendan. Colm was driving me through Killarney on a day when Cork had triumphed in a Munster final in Fitzgerald stadium. The streets were awash with red and white, The Banks and the Boys of Fair Hill were heard on every side. The native population had disappeared in the face of such triumphalism. "Jaysus," said Colm, "I hate losing to Cork, Corkmen are lousy winners."

Mid-afternoon the world stopped. God only knows what tourists and visitors thought as the population vanished and an eerie silence fell over mountain, valley and coast. A little pressure on our hearts early on was followed by a growing feeling that things were going to be alright, the world was not ending.

Kerry people are good winners and magnanimous in victory. Cork were worthy opponents and when their turn comes, as it assuredly will, I ask God to let it be in the distant future in a year when Kerry are taking a rest. The cup came to Glenbeigh on Tuesday night, borne by the captain and the men who won the day. The vast crowd assembled will never forget the evening. Finn, sitting on his mountain Seefin (Suí Finn) above Glenbeigh, will have been happy with the champions he sent forth, and who, unlike the incompetents he sent to capture Diarmuid and Gráinne, were successful in their quest. Ceann Comhairle John O'Donoghue was to have been MC at the homecoming but reluctantly the people decided they couldn't afford him.

Maybe we can give our Cork friends a new verse for 'Fair Hill'?

> *The lads from Cork were full of glee*
> *They'd bring Sam back to the Lee*
> *Here's up them all, said the boys of Ciarraí*

I can go and vote Yes to Lisbon with a light heart.

September 29th, 2009

A true tale about men and stupidity

Varium et mutabile semper femina
(Virgil)

Mercury seemingly said this to Aeneas in a vision. Virgil had the sense not to claim the observation as his own lest Mrs Virgil took offence at the intimation "that a woman is always a fickle unstable thing". The Roman Sisterhood would certainly have taken umbrage, so Virgil placed the phrase in the mouth of a fictional character. Wasn't he the clever poet? I am about to tell you a true story and as this concerns the Highest Authority, I would be obliged if you could keep it to yourselves. It starts with the stupidity of men, as so many tales do. In this case it was me.

The HA was destined to attend her school reunion dinner and I, with a Lesser Authority and a newly-arrived grandson, were left to fend for ourselves. Ever resourceful, I suggested to my daughter that we should avail of the menu in a local takeaway in Blackrock village; furthermore that we should select a nice bottle of wine and maybe watch some rugby on the box, thus proving that in dire emergency we could take care of ourselves. The order was placed and I duly set forth to collect same.

It was a very bad night, with gale force wind and torrential rain. I briefly considered taking the car, but in deference to carbon emissions or some theory like that, I equipped myself with hat, raincoat and umbrella and, like Scott of the Antarctic, set forth bravely into the darkness. As I turned into the teeth of the gale on the Rock Road, my hat blew off and the umbrella turned inside out. I retrieved the hat, fixed the umbrella and plodded grimly towards my destination. There was not a solitary Christian to be seen abroad, as I plodded along keeping close to the wall to avoid the spray from passing cars.

I obtained brief respite when I reached the Blackrock Centre, having lost the hat several times and with an umbrella that didn't seem to know which side should face the elements. A short dash down Main Street and I reached my goal, collected my order and set off for home. The weather was now worse, and I had the additional problem of keeping the dinner dry.

Now for those who don't know the area, I will explain that at the junction of Mount Merrion Avenue and Rock Road there is a perpetual puddle which on this evening had assumed the proportions of a lake. As I had to pass this, I paused until no vehicle was in sight and then moved forwards quickly. The umbrella did its trick again and my hat sailed into the lake. It reached the shore on the far side and as I arrived to retrieve it, a person driving an 09 BMW at 90 miles an hour went straight through the lake. If that driver still lives, there is nothing in the power of prayer. I made it home, saturated and with a soggy dinner. Outside the house was a car collecting the HA for her dinner. She took one look at me and, you won't believe this, she laughed.

The following Tuesday morning I was late putting out the green bin. I hoped that the collection would be later than usual, but on my return from golf in the afternoon it was still full. I left it there. About an hour later the HA returned from her golf. In Dublin we do not play in the same club, but I won't go into that in case some liberal decides to name and shame me. In any case the HA did not seem to be in the best of humours. We men tend to notice such things, as we are very sensitive to sudden drops in room temperature. I said nothing and eventually the cause was revealed. It was my fault.

She had pulled up to the gates of the house and opened them with the remote control. She got out of the car and, finding the green bin full, dragged it into the garden. As she turned around the gate was closing and she rushed to get through. She was too late and got stuck in the gate. Her remote control was in the car and she could not reach the panel on the gate pillar. It was raining heavily. A kind taxi driver noted her predicament and liberated her. If I had put the green bin out in time, none of this would have happened.
Something similar must have happened to Virgil.

November 24th, 2009

This winter, it seems it never rains but it pours

It's a bitterly cold day here in Kerry. The surrounding mountains are all snowcapped. We have been warned that more snow may be on the way. It is low tide and the Highest Authority and I have just walked the length of the beach. Apart from the occasional, quickly passing hail shower, it is a beautiful afternoon in a beautiful place. The HA is incapable of sitting still and taking a day off from exercise. I have no such problem, although I know and believe that a modicum of daily exercise is an essential part of keeping active and healthy. Quite apart from that the HA does not let me sit still for more than 30 minutes at a time. At weekends I have another powerful motive – my exercise justifies my pint.

Shortly after our return to Dublin after Christmas, having been duly exercised and with the prospect of being fed, I was reading the Sunday newspapers suffused by a feeling of wellbeing. That as you all know is not a good thing. The phone rang and a neighbour of ours in Kerry inquired if our house was alright.

He explained that it was snowing heavily and that while checking some houses he had encountered a litany of problems. I assured him that we had taken all our usual precautions before we left and that over the years we had never had weather-related troubles. This failed to convince him, he said he'd check anyway and headed out into the snow and gathering gloom.

I then had to translate this conversation to the HA, who assumed from the odd word she picked up that some natural disaster had occurred. Had I switched off the immersion heater? Had I set the central heating for background heat? Had I turned off the water? I might point out that none of these tasks ever fell to me before. I am barely qualified with the vacuum cleaner and have only a provisional licence to fill the dishwasher.

I explained patiently that no disaster had occurred and that Paul was simply being a good neighbour. The phone rang again almost immediately and made a liar out of me. Paul told me that looking through one of the windows he could see water cascading down a light fitting into a little hallway. Where were the keys? Where were the stopcocks? All decision-making was instantly removed from my hands and the competent folk got on with it.

I was quickly assured that the problem had been dealt with in time and that damage was slight. There is a problem with perception here. The HA felt that it was clearly a flood of biblical proportions. My failure to concede this was taken as wilful stubbornness overlaid by guilt for allowing the mishap to occur at all. Some days passed and our neighbour rang to say all was in hand and that necessary repairs had been effected.

He was so positive that I passed the call on to the HA so that she might be reassured. After a couple of minutes I heard her say, "You can't be serious". There was actually a small prayer before that remark. My antennae felt that this boded ill. She turned a tragic face to me and announced that there were "rats as big as cats" in the attic. I said a quick prayer for our good neighbour and weakly opined that it wasn't the end of the world. That wasn't the cleverest remark I've ever made.

To cut a long story short, here we are in Kerry with all repaired and not a rat in sight. However, the spectre of Leptospirosis and possibly Weil's syndrome had been raised and had to be taken seriously. Rats can shed the causative organism in their urine for months after exposure, and quite apart from eliminating the rats it is necessary to clean everything that could be contaminated. It is rare, 100 cases or so in the US yearly, but there may be more people affected sub-clinically.

It has been a severe winter and the rodents have sought warmth and shelter. Well, they can look somewhere else and not be causing me grief. If they exist here at all they have enough rat poison presented to them to clear the entire country. I am going to challenge the fates and observe that peace has been restored and that furthermore I have attained a modest degree of proficiency in scrubbing and cleaning. This wasn't quite how I had envisaged retirement but there you are.

March 2nd, 2010

Volcanic dust settles our life on the ocean wave

By thy long grey beard and
glittering eye
Now wherefore stopp'st thou me

I'll tell you why. I am about to relate a tale of shipwreck, riot, piracy, storm, eruption and the marooning of a group of intrepid mariners. This is related by Maurice (Sinbad) N and his consort HA (Polo) N, and given under their hand in this year of Our Lord 2010. The truth of all I tell is attested by our worthy companions, Jaki from the New Forest, and Peter and Jean, mighty seafarers from Guernsey.

At the outset of my tale, the HA and I were wafted on a magic carpet to the fabled city of Hong Kong in the ancient civilisation of Cathay. It is no longer a dark and mysterious land. It is open and friendly and well able to trade beads with the rest of us. Having joined our frail barque in the port, we set sail for exotic lands. Very soon, disaster struck. Our simple six-course meal was interrupted by a shuddering crash. "What was that?" we wondered in our

Titanic complacency, "bit warm for icebergs." It was in fact a collision with a Star Ferry vessel, boats which ply their purposes in these crowded waters. The captain and crew laboured to repair the non-existent damage and soon we were under way again.

On days at sea, to appease the restless traders, strange rituals were enacted. One such involved dividing us into groups of six and asking us difficult and diverse questions. The winning team would gain riches beyond avarice, a bookmark for example. We were teamed with an Australian lady, a Russian couple, both mathematicians, and our American leader. On one occasion I brought shame and ridicule upon our group. On being asked what mythical creature wore white gloves, red shirt and yellow trousers, in conclave our group decided the answer was one Mickey Mouse. "No," I insisted, "that is too obvious, the true answer must be our great Irish statesman Bertie Ahern." Okay, I was wrong, but I philosophised in the current nonsensical phrase of our homeland, "same difference".

St Patrick's Day found us in Ho Chi Minh City (Saigon). I was conscious that a great Irish leader called Conor Lenihan was due to honour the city on our national day. The inhabitants seemed slightly underwhelmed by this, although there were some banners stretched across minor roads. Upon inquiring upon their import our guide, however, told us they appeared to be advertising some form of kebabs. Bangkok found us in the midst of riots with gangs of red-shirted individuals seemingly intent on bringing down the government. Mind you, compared with us Irish, they appeared to have little to complain about. Maybe we might try that soon!

Exotic locations followed one another. The Maldives were still there and prospering despite global warming, as were the Seychelles. Our next port was to be Mombasa and then inland to the Masai Mara to trade rhinoceros horn and ivory and then to rejoin our ship in Zanzibar laden down with the treasures of Africa.

Unfortunately, our captain dolefully informed us that the Somali pirates were happily cutting throats in the sea lanes we were about to traverse and, accordingly, we fled southwards to Mauritius and Reunion. In Reunion, I visited the volcanoes and even the volcano museum. I became an instant vulcanologist. Indeed, I think I know as much about it as the experts who have just paralysed the world.

We ploughed through tropical storm "Robin" when many took to their beds fearing the end of creation. Many fasted that night voluntarily or otherwise. The HA wondered at my "iron stomach". I explained that I was both hungry and thirsty and that if I was going to drown, I'd sooner go full and happy. That impressed her.

Finally, our trading came to an end. Iceland blew up and we were marooned in Capetown. We were given enough bread and water to last one week but fortunately on the sixth day we were rescued and returned to Thief Row (aka Heathrow). I understand if by now you have had enough of this maritime tale and would say in Coleridge's 'Rime of the Ancient Mariner', already quoted:

> *'Hold off, unhand me grey-beard loon!',*
> *Eftsoons his hand dropped he*

I'll drop my pen also, to pick it up again next week. There is work to be done in our little island.

April 27th, 2010

A beautiful day to keep the brambles at bay

It is a lovely summer day. A hint of a westerly wind pushes the cups of the anemometer. It is warm, with enough fluffy wandering clouds to provide some shade. I am writing outdoors. I remember, in far-off days of examinations in medical school, that I and two close friends would avail of such weather to leave the city and study in some quiet, secluded place. Such peaceful environments worked for us. Some of our colleagues could only study when alone. Some sought a cool dark room. Others could work with a radio or television in the background. Some were early birds, others worked late into the night. One hardy man would study in Hartigan's pub from five to eight most evenings before the arrival of hordes of thirsty students rendered such exercise futile.

Irrespective of location, concentration and willpower were essential attributes. Without them you were wasting your time. All three of our little group became surgeons. One was my best man when the HA removed me from random circulation, and the other was a groomsman. One is dead and the other has a long-term illness. I am left with memories – kind memories of great friends. I can see them clearly in these quiet surroundings, and I say a little prayer for them from my innermost being.

I started the day swimming in calm unruffled water on a full tide. Sounds were magnified across the water: cattle lowing, a dog barking, faint voices carried from far away. I emerged from the deep, energy renewed and ready to face whatever the world, more particularly the HA, would ordain for the rest of the day.

Today, it started with brambles. There is a long lane leading to the house and the brambles here have a nasty habit of growing. Seemingly, they can scratch the paintwork of passing cars. Secateurs in hand, I set out. It could have been worse. On a beautiful morning in such a tranquil place, the work proceeded very slowly. There were too many distractions to concentrate on the job in hand. There were butterflies, large and small white. There were the less plentiful red admirals heading for the nettle patches where they lay their eggs. There were dragonflies with helicopter-like facility of vertical flight. There were myriad swallows strafing the road as they snapped up insects on the wing. These were ideal stimuli to make the worker lean on his spade and postpone the designated work. Observing this joyous carnival of life and growth made progress very slow.

R fruticosus or bramble or blackberry behave like triffids around here. The many-headed Hydra has nothing on them. No sooner was one shoot severed than three more sprang into its place. We are going to have a major crop this year. They range from the white flowers to green fruit, ripening to red, with the odd precocious black one thrown in. The blackberry picking, done happily in younger years, is less welcome in your earned dotage, but it is inescapable because the HA makes jam. There are 400 varieties of blackberry, and they vary widely in texture and taste. I haven't a clue what variety ours are other than they are black and go into jam. They have to be picked before Michaelmas because everybody knows that on that night the Devil pisses on the brambles, rendering the fruit inedible. Mind you, I haven't seen that myself, but have occasionally witnessed something similar on golf courses throughout the country. Nobody wanted to eat those blackberries either.

Brambles were planted in graveyards to deter grazing sheep and to keep the dead interred and the Devil outside. The long, thorny stems were also known as "lawyers" because of the painful difficulties in trying to escape their clutches. They are also sometimes planted near young trees to guard against the depredations of grazing deer. As we've only ever had the one deer it would seem to us to be an unnecessary precaution. It is also claimed that brambles in some mysterious way confer some protection against hernias.

The HA finally appeared, noted that I had failed to deal with the problem adequately once again and, what was more, I had taken hours to achieve so little. All right, so I didn't do a great job on the brambles, but I was at peace and had thoroughly enjoyed myself. Another magic day raced away, as they do in this idyllic spot in Kerry.

August 3rd, 2010

A ramble along the warm valley of recollection

We are enjoying a late flourish of summer in this little enclave in Co Kerry. It is too late for many visitors who have to return to the real world. The local wildlife re-emerges now to claim their lands, happy that the laughing children and city dogs are no longer here. The children are facing back to school, harassed mothers talking uniforms and books and in every way more practical than glum fathers facing departure from this magical place. That's the trouble with fairyland. It fades away. We are afforded glimpses and veiled promises that it will return. The hope sustains, in the uncertain world that faces many today.

In my working life, the sadness of departure left me as I crossed the Co Kerry border. I did not dwell on what I had left behind. The focus became the work ahead, the patients, the operations, the entire fabric of a different life, professionally and socially. For most folk that is the pattern of life, work and earned relaxation. I had little reason to regret such ordering of existence. I was luckier than many.

119

Now in retirement from the treadmill, it is possible to sit back and think about different things. This morning we had breakfast outdoors in the sunshine. The calm, motionless waters mirrored the surrounding hills. Sitting there in peace, quiet and absolute stillness, the doors of memory opened. Memories tend to come in haphazard fashion – they are seldom layered precisely and you have to order them yourself. You can't live in the halls of memory or rather you should not try. The world is present and future and, in the immortal words of Ivor Callely, "Yesterday's history".

The pathway starts with a word or a phrase, "Do you remember?", and then you are off on your journey. The trip can be wide ranging and diffuse or localised and specific, but it should not be lightly undertaken. You need to be strong to go there and to balance the good, the bad and the sad. To the honest traveller, these all present themselves and suppression seldom works.

This particular foray was focused on the 30 years or so that we have been coming here. Initially, there was never enough time for the activities of the day. We made firm and lasting friendships and became mutual part-guardians for the layers of children that mushroomed around us. We knew 99 per cent of everything and in retrospect we all took ourselves more seriously than reason would allow. This was going to last forever. We deferred to our seniors, we looked after them and we included them. In retrospect, we were a condescending shower. Our children, endlessly parsed and analysed and we thought, properly supervised, lived in their own world with its own rules, priorities and hierarchies as they grew, season by season, all around us.

The trouble was that day by day, holiday by holiday, imperceptively, we all grew older. These Elysian Fields were not to be ours forever, in this world at least. The vitality and strength that had carried us so confidently through the years of raising the family, slowly waned and we found ourselves catapulted into the category of senior citizens. One of the first intimations of this for me came when descending the steps of Skellig Michael in a measured manner, a polite young American inquired, "Are you alright, sir?" I bit my lip, thanked him and assured him that I was really a gazelle taking things easy.

The children so carefully nurtured and supervised were now condescendingly and obviously looking out for us. They laughingly told us escapades, hitherto unknown, that would have given us sleepless nights. I learned belatedly that "a few pints" meant up to six; "a rake of pints" covered six to 12 and that "a feed of pints" went from there to dissolution; and we thought we were hard men! They're all growing strong and solid around us, our own and those whose guardianship we were privileged to share. There are grandchildren unloaded for us to mind and we now, in pasture, witness the same strength and certainty that we thought was ours forever. The pleasant ramble along the warm valleys of recollection inevitably brings you to the shadows, the memories of those gone. They are good memories, but sometimes they can be overwhelmingly sad. There are no hiding places on this road.

August 31st, 2010

TIMES PAST

Journey round my youth

I suppose one cannot be critical of everything in the health services all the time. This is particularly so as my experience of dealing with its different strands over many years has essentially been positive. You could not meet kinder and more concerned people than I found at all levels in the caring professions. The same was true of those who were trying to administer a chaotic system. The faults, in so far as they are now discoverable, lay elsewhere. But more of that later.

Looking back is easy; you may conveniently forget the bad times and indulge in nostalgic remembrance of the good. I shall, however, endeavour to recall my passage into medicine, and then surgery, reflect upon the past and then possibly speculate on future directions.

I was born in Booterstown, Co Dublin, in May 1937. I was a domiciliary birth - not uncommon then - and was delivered by Dr Joe Stuart, later president of the GAA and a friend of my parents. It was on the afternoon of Whit Sunday, a fact which led my mother to expect that I would acquire the gift of tongues. I did, to some extent, but the influence of my father may have been stronger. An army officer, he had served in the merchant marine in the first World War.

Although unaware at the time, it was probably my first exposure to the nature versus nurture argument which has dogged me to this day. I do not intend to inflict upon you the story of an essentially happy childhood but, looking back, it was a seminal time in the formation of the Ireland of today which our parents and grandparents' generations were then formulating and which, understandably but undeniably, shaped our attitudes.

In that TV-free age, reading was all important and to me has remained one of the great pleasures in life. We had certainly a less protected and freer lifestyle because many of the difficulties and problems of today were unheard of, indeed undreamt of. Sadly we know now that even then bad things were happening, things that only now are coming to light. As I did not set out to write an autobiography in this article, I will move on to explain - if possible - how I arrived at my present position.

I was dispatched to school in Willow Park preparatory school and then through to Blackrock College. I can honestly say, throughout that passage, I was extremely happy and I owe a debt of gratitude to the priests and teachers of Blackrock that I can never repay. Friendships formed in those years and later in university (where I discovered that some nice people existed who hadn't been to Blackrock) remain central to my life. I had two great ambitions in Blackrock. Firstly, I wanted to be a great rugby player. Secondly, I wished to be able to sing. Sadly, despite strenuous endeavours, I only obtained mediocrity in both and had to settle for becoming a cardiac surgeon.

I did not, as noted earlier, come from a medical family, although one brother-in-law became professor of anatomy in UCD. My interest in doing medicine came about through my reading, coupled with my complete naivety. Axel Munthe and AJ Cronin were amongst the writers who inspired me, with Richard Gordon for the lighter side of medicine. Thus I resolved to become a doctor.

In my final year in Blackrock, we were all individually summoned to our dean, Father Finucane. When my turn came he inquired of me what I wished to do in life. I explained and there was a long silence. Then he spoke: "Next to the church, I think that would be a reasonable thing to do. Have you ever considered the priesthood?" Another long silence, this time on my part as I wished I was elsewhere. Eventually I muttered some inanities about not having a vocation and was permitted to withdraw.

Leaving Certificate and Matriculation exams, which would decide if you could follow your chosen career, were ahead. The academic requirements then were much less stringent than today. There was no points system. Was this a good thing or not? On balance I think it probably was good, as cramming was unnecessary and therefore more rounded individuals emerged. It must be conceded that medicine now is more technical and scientific and that higher basic standards may be required.

However, such high standards and points may obscure the vocation necessary for the profession and the attainment of the points may not per se guarantee a fulfilled career. For us the requirement, along with our Leaving Cert and/or Matriculation (NUI), was that we had Latin, English, Mathematics and Irish. Trinity College was not an option for many of us in that era of the closed mind. The Royal College of Surgeons existed, but sounded faintly exotic. For my classmates and I, our eyes were fixed on UCD.

Life, you know, is really a series of ladders: you climb one and become monarch of all you survey, then find yourself at the bottom rung of the next. Thus I found myself, with great regret, leaving my safe haven in Blackrock and venturing out into the challenging and, I hoped, exciting world of the medical student. I was not to be disappointed.

February 24th, 2004

A bygone
era of innocence

Having diverted myself, if that is the appropriate word, into the dissecting room and also to other related issues, I must point out this was a limited part of the life of a medical student. The academic bit was inescapable - well almost - and formal lectures and practicals took up nine to six, Monday to Friday, and would you believe nine to one on Saturdays. European working time directive how are ye! There were gaps of course which prudently should be spent in the library. Why is it that the virtues like prudence are so hard to obtain whereas the vices seem to just come naturally?

It was a different time and a different Dublin. For the student, there was little in the line of sophisticated entertainment and, in any case, most of us had little money. Some went to the theatre (usually the gods - do those Olympian heights still exist?). More went to the cinema, often during lecture hours, and the sports grounds - and sports facilities were there for the more active. There were no such things as nightclubs at our level and a late night party was as good as it got. You usually brought your own provisions, six Guinness in a brown paper bag being the usual offering.

The rumour of such an event attracted hundreds of the uninvited after closing time but there was rarely any trouble. To this day, however, I retain a great respect for those who gave these functions, as the venue flat or house must have been uninhabitable for weeks afterwards. Incidentally, there seemed to be no such thing then as an apartment. Is that a posher word for a flat? For us, the whole known world within a radius of one mile centred on St Stephen's Green.

There were, it is true, rumours of strange lands and peoples beyond the pale but they were not germane to life within our cocoon. Dances in clubs, usually rugby and in various ballrooms around the city, permitted social intermingling. I unwittingly nearly caused the demise of my children from paroxysms of laughter when I referred to these events as "hops". I retreated rapidly into my geriatric shell. I remember also the Metropole, the Crystal, the Olympic and the Four Provinces (rather risqué that one).

The formal faculty and club dances were very important also. No question of going on your own or with the lads. There was not even a sharing option; the gentleman paid for the lot, tickets, flowers, chocolates and with little expectation. We really were an innocent lot. The above arrangement now, with the rise of the sisterhood, seems archaic but I suppose everything changes. There were other peculiarities also. Most had been taught ballroom dancing formally and you actually held your partner. If you remember Earl Gill or Neil Kearns, you know the world I am referring to.

If, on the other hand, you belong to the school who stand in the midst of ear-splitting discord and gesticulate at each other, then you can only thank me how far you have evolved. The days of the disco deafness tribunals I suppose are not too far off. The centre of the universe contained all we needed and could afford. The pubs like Hartigans (women only tolerated on the night of final medical results), the Lincoln Inn and a few more were more than adequate for our simple needs.

The latest legislation will convert them all into oases of clean air to which the citizens can fly to escape the fumes and pollution outside. I suppose this was the intention of our modest Minister for Health all along and that those who felt he should shore up the collapsing health service first have got it all wrong. We lead the world. Hooray! And we have got the lads on the trolleys off the front pages. We never had to queue for a pub, a phenomenon I saw only recently. I pointed out to my brood that there did not seem to me to be a shortage of pubs in Ireland and was informed condescendingly that these were the "in" places. The problems of our world we did not see or choose to see. They were not as now the problems of affluence but of poverty, chronic unemployment, emigration and inadequate educational opportunity.

It was a deeply conservative society, rigid and inflexible. Nowhere was this more apparent than in medicine, where the first State intrusions into a hierarchial and proprietorial system were treated with suspicion and outright hostility. As medical students we were scarcely aware of this, but on our arrival on the wards we very soon would be.

April 6th, 2004

Survival of the meanest

The resident year as a medical student in the Mater in the late 1950s was an interesting one. Resident was a misnomer, as apart from one month during the year we did not actually live in the hospital. The rest of the time you made your way to the hospital for the start of the day's work. Hospitals rise early and most clinical units were at work by 8 a.m. This fact of life, however, only became a reality for us after graduation, and thankfully did not extend to our student days.

More latitude was allowed us then, basically because we were useless appendages of the system, bottom feeders and expected to be grateful for any scraps of knowledge incidentally acquired. We did, however, have limited duties - we took the bloods. We were the phlebotomists. Anybody now acquainted with hospital life and accustomed to having their blood taken for tests, by accomplished business-like women, deadly efficient in all they do, will know what a real phlebotomist is.

We were not like that. For starters, we were not trained as such and we learned from watching each other. This is not the best way to learn, but it was all that was available to us. As in every facet of life, there are quick learners and slow learners, there are those who are adept with their hands, and some less so, some even clumsy. It did not seem to concern the powers that be, and we were left with the problems of extracting given amounts of blood from particular patients, making sure it was placed in the appropriate containers and delivered to the laboratory. On the face of it, this seems reasonably simple. It was not so at the time.

It was your first duty of the day. You presented yourself in your then clean white coat on your ward as early as possible in the morning and your intern (another form of medical low-life) would present you with a list of patients from whom blood was to be taken, and the various blood tests required.

On the surgical side of the hospital, this was usually not too bad. On the medical side, where the lordly physicians were investigating all sorts of abstruse conditions, this could be a monumental job. It would not have been at all unusual to have a list of 20 to 30 victims - I mean patients - requiring your attention. I am not talking leeches here, nor cupping and bleeding, as in days of yore, merely taking enough blood for diagnostic purposes.

The next step was the execution of the task. The instruments we had available to us at that time bore no relation to those available today. Everything we used, excepting the swabs, had to be sterilised after each patient, and re-used. The syringes were of glass in varying sizes, and the accidental breakage of same was almost a capital offence. In some hospitals the students had to pay for replacements and the very least you could expect was an unpleasant interview with the dragon (Sister) who ran the ward. The needles (of steel) were of varying length, thickness and sharpness. Come early and you got the pick, come later and you would be guaranteed some bad friends amongst the patients.

You then set forth, with your little tray, to inject some misery into the patients' lives. This, of course, was not the intention but sadly often the result. We usually started in the male wards, having been told that it is easier to get blood from men. It is, but I suppose you don't have to be a medical student to appreciate that - just take a look around in daily life. In the strictly anatomical sense, this was because the distribution of body fat made the veins of the man more apparent on the surface.

You approached your victim with an air of nonchalance, applied a tourniquet on the arm and instructed the patient to clench their fist several times. This brought the veins in the forearm and elbow into relief. It was then a simple matter to slip the needle into the vein, withdraw the plunger on the syringe, extract the blood, fill and label your little bottles and dispatch the lot to the laboratory.

That was the theory, and it worked, provided the needle was not blocked, and was actually located within a vein, and that the plunger of the syringe was not too tight or too loose. It worked if your patient had any visible veins, that had not been previously destroyed by hordes of vampire students, and if they were not so unlucky as to have any visible veins at all.

Then it was bad for us, and it must have been frightful for the patients. Failure to acquire the blood was simply not an option, and sometimes a more adept student blood diviner would be called upon by his fellows to locate more deeply hidden streams. Curses, maledictions and prayers filled the ward as we stuck grimly to our task, leaving bruises on arms and hands to mark our passage. The moral for any patient out there is "never be in a doctor's first 100 of anything, if you can possibly avoid it". Quite what observance of that precept would do for medical pioneering, I am unsure, but we and most of the patients survived.

June 29th, 2004

Dealing with dying

When I started to write about my residence year as a student, and all that it involved, I began to understand how fundamental it was to our collective future careers. My memory does not enlighten me as to whether we thought so at the time. There is a dichotomy between the everyday experiences and the meaning of it all. Reason tells me, the latter did not trouble us unduly at the time.

This was our initial point of patient contact and we began, for the first time, to experience the intricacies of the doctor-patient relationship. We found that there were faults on both sides of this line, particularly in an implicit assumption that the medical participant is a good listener. Not all medical people are, and this became obvious to us as students. Sympathy and understanding were not universal traits among the profession, nor indeed among ourselves. Entering fully into the life, this became obvious in our daily contact with patients.

We did of course do more than just draw blood. We took case histories and conducted physical examinations, what was called clerking the patient. We attended outpatients and the accident and emergency department. ER it was not. Everything was new, everything was interesting, and our knowledge base was gradually and ever so slowly expanding.

Most of us encountered death for the first time, either abruptly in A&E or more slowly, but just as finally in the wards. We learned the obvious differences between those slipping away quietly in old age, and the bitter loss of husband or wife in mid-life, and the heartbreak of the death of a child. Thomas Mann noted that "A man's dying is more the survivors' affair than his own."

We learned the very hard lesson that a doctor could not function properly if a certain detachment from the tragedy of others was not maintained. This is often interpreted as callousness or indifference on the part of the doctor. It seldom is. It is the necessary carapace, constructed to keep one functioning dispassionately in order to help the next in line.

We learned the wide spectrum of grief reactions, and to try to understand them, even when the whole focus was on real or perceived failure by our profession. This was not an easy part of our education, not to be learned from books, and before the advent of counselling, and organised chaplaincy services. We were amateurs and, as usual, we learned from our nursing colleagues and above all from the good Sisters.

These nursing Sisters were a race apart, and their decline in numbers leaves a gap, impossible to fill adequately. For everyone else in the profession, the caring is part of your life, for the Sisters it was their entire calling.

I would not like anybody to think that we spent our time contemplating mortality, but it did impinge upon our lives. I well remember a young intern who refused to certify a young man as dead. He maintained that he was only asleep; he had to be led away while a colleague saw to the formalities. People do die inappropriately, and we, who would have to face this repeatedly, were building our own self-defence mechanisms in order to avoid the contagion of grief. This is all very heavy and gloomy and, of course, it was not always all doom. Patients did survive occasionally and, in the words of Meyer Perelstein, "If your time hasn't come, not even a doctor can kill you."

I well remember being allotted my first patient to treat. The consultant who headed our team at the time, told me to examine a patient in an outpatient cubicle, to arrive at a diagnosis, to read up the treatment and to write a prescription. If he agreed with it all, he would sign the prescription. I quickly established that the patient was a guest of the State, across the road in Mountjoy, and was suffering from an infestation with a tapeworm.

I read up on the treatment and duly presented the scrip to the chief for signature. He looked mildly surprised and suggested I discuss this with the hospital pharmacist. This I did, and this kindly man asked me if I was intent on purging a horse. I indignantly replied that the treatment regime had been taken directly from the bible of therapeutics. He asked me to produce the book and when I did so, he filled the prescription remarking that he was glad he was not the patient. I returned to the outpatient department and delivered medication and instructions to the patient. It transpired that he was due for release two days later and intended travelling to England the following day. I assured him that this would not be a problem.

Five days later on entering the outpatients again, I was hailed by a skeleton, sitting on one of the benches. It was my patient, two stone lighter, with sunken cheeks and hollowed eyes. He had missed his boat and required a letter to explain same. As he put it succinctly: "Jaysus, doctor, if I had any loose teeth, I would have lost them." However, we got the tapeworm.

July 6th, 2004

A little bit of theatre

Recent controversies involving the Minister for Health and almost every branch of the medical profession prompts a revisit of the old story about the proud mother watching her son in the passing-out parade for a group of army recruits. "Look father, they're all out of step but our Johnny." Matters political and medico-political, are not, thankfully, the whole world, and I can take refuge in memory and reminiscence, which although sometimes selective, cannot be altered.

> *The moving finger writes; and having writ*
> *Moves on; nor all your Piety nor Wit*
> *Shall lure it back to cancel half a line*
> *Nor all your Tears wash out a Word of it.*

Fitzgerald's 'Rubayiat of Omar Khayyam' simply expresses the fact that the past cannot be altered, although it may be re-interpreted.

But to return to the incontrovertible and unimportant happenings of my student days. The last installation culminated with my success in curing the patient with the tapeworm, which occurred during my resident year as a medical student. Lots of other memories of that first hospital year come back to me. It was very demanding, particularly in university term time when we not only had our hospital duties in the mornings, but also lectures in the afternoon.

To add to your woes, you might then be rostered for casualty or hospital cover that night. It was not, of course, that our presence in the hospital or casualty department was necessary, or possibly even desirable, but it was one of the best ways to learn about patients and hospital life. In this year also, we received our initiation into the new world of operating theatres. I did not realise the operating theatre was the place I was to spend most of my working life.

Some of my fellow students did not like this environment; some were indifferent and some were; like myself, fascinated. At first, in theatre you were in everybody's way. The awkwardness started with changing from everyday clothes and white coat into theatre scrubs. As the student changing room was small, this was akin to six people changing simultaneously in a telephone box. Footwear consisted of plastic overshoes, or you inherited ancient clogs or rubber boots. Some of this ancient footwear dated back to Viking times and a fatal dose of athlete's foot was an ever-present possibility. A face mask and a cap or hood - more likely the latter, since these were our long-haired years - completed the outfit. These were cotton and re-usable. There were few disposable items in those days.

Finally, fully changed and feeling very self-conscious, you ventured forth into this busy, brightly-lit world, where everybody else seemed to know what they were doing. As for consultant surgeons, they were really gods and could not be expected to notice insect life.

Finally, someone would notice the huddled group of students. "Which of you is working for Mr X?" You would suddenly realise that you were in the firing line and grimly acknowledge your presence. "You will be needed to scrub up and assist." A brief prayer - "O Jesus, let me not make a complete balls of this," - and on rubbery legs you took the next step, to be initiated into the mysteries of washing hands and forearms in a sterile fashion and then donning your surgical gown and rubber gloves.

This sounds relatively easy, but believe me, it wasn't, or otherwise I was seriously deficient. The basic premise was to keep the unwashed non-sterile bits away from the washed, gowned and gloved you. As a gentle exercise, try putting on your gloves without touching the outside. We must have de-sterilised enough gloves, gowns and drapes to affect the hospital budget for years to come. Our instructors, usually nurses, tended to get exasperated and impatient as we, at what then seemed the nadir of our careers, struggled to put gloves on five-thumbed hands.

If you were unlucky, the operation would be over before you joined the fray and you became even more an object of ridicule and contempt. Otherwise, finally cleaned and dressed, like the turkey, you were propelled towards the action. "Touch nothing other than the green drapes," you were commanded. "Oh God, you clown, come back here and scrub again."

In time, we became more comfortable and less maladroit and even, dare I say it, useful. The interest grew with the involvement. It was then that I knew I wanted to be a surgeon.

July 27th, 2004

A little hospital humour

Previously, I have described my initiation into the world of the operating theatre. Little did I know at the time that it would prove the locus of my future professional life. At this stage in our training, the fascination of medicine was taking hold. There was more to come in other core branches of the profession: obstetrics, paediatrics, pathology, forensic medicine and so on. The sheer volume of knowledge to be absorbed for your future career, not to mention the more immediate problem of examinations, was daunting. At the time, in our resident student year, medicine and surgery were our principal pre-occupations, but we also had parallel lectures on such riveting subjects as social and preventive medicine, and in microbiology.

There was nothing in these subjects that held student interest in comparison to the daily happenings in the hospitals, but we realised that they were part of the foundations, and while they were not there to be enjoyed, they had to be endured. Microbiology and pathology were, in fact, closely integrated with our teaching, and both were vital to the understanding of the spectrum of illness that we encountered daily.

We tried hard and diligently, but our haloes slipped occasionally and the odd lecture was skipped, particularly on fine, sunny days. I remember well a large section of our class being released unexpectedly into the sunshine from a dismal lecture on medical statistics. A student in one of the middle rows of the tiered lecture hall was quietly reading the newspaper when a friend in the row below quietly lit the lower edge of the paper, and the lecture hall was enveloped in smoke, flames and curses. Guilty and innocent alike were ejected into the sunshine with dire threats of retribution at exam time.

I also remember, with mixed feelings, that on presenting myself in the out-patient department one morning, the staff nurse who normally would not deign to notice students, said to me: "I thought you were on holidays." "No," I assured her. Sometime later, an intern made a similar remark. Finally, the consultant came in and said: "I am delighted to see Mr Neligan, you are honouring us with your presence." There was laughter from all, except yours truly. Similar remarks continued throughout the morning, until finally a fellow student told me to look at the social and personal columns of the morning newspapers.

It was then the custom for senior consultants leaving on holiday to notify these columns of their absence. This custom persisted until they realised that with literacy on the increase, many burglars could now read. In any case, at the end of the usual list of holiday arrangements, there I was. "Maurice C Neligan, clinical clerk and surgical dresser, will be out of town for a short period." Indeed, I had some nice classmates.

Those subjected to our medical humour didn't always see the funny side and the humorist was often landed in trouble with the powers that be. A colleague, now a highly respected GP, provided two such light moments. He was dealing with a very overweight lady who was complaining of vague abdominal pain. Persistent questioning failed to pinpoint a definite location, as it seemed to move all over the abdomen. Exasperated, he hazarded a diagnosis. "I think, Mrs So and So, that you are suffering from a wandering fart." Instant outrage and severe reprimands were visited on our classmate. Undaunted, our intrepid hero struck again, this time dealing with a man complaining of altered bowel habit. Had he passed blood? Negative. Had he had diarrhoea? Negative. Was he constipated? Well, sort of. "What do you mean by that?" asked my colleague. "Well," said the patient, "the motions are small and hard and kind of diamond shaped." Quick as a flash, our budding doctor arrived at the solution: "I suggest, sir, that you cut six inches off your string vest."

It may surprise you to know that we were an irreverent shower, but such events helped to preserve sanity, in situations where humour was rare. Now, I am going to be politically incorrect. We learned that while doctors could be bad, patients could be 10 times worse. We learned the difficult, dangerous and inexact art of distinguishing the hypochondriac from the genuinely ill.

We learned also how to deal with the difficult patients. You would tell these patients that everything they were telling you was very important, so important you wanted them to go home and write it all down exactly as it happened and bring it back next week. When they had completed the task, you would say: "Thank you very much, I will have to read these 20 pages very carefully, come back next week for your prescription." You don't have to be a rocket scientist to figure out the rest.

Look suspiciously at your doctor the next time you visit to see if there is a glint in his or her eye. If not, maybe choose another doctor.

August 3rd, 2004

A life of non-stop learning

Time carries all things, even our wits, away
(Virgil)

Memory is indeed fallible and recollection of the events of 40 years ago can be difficult, as I have found of late. So much so, that I feel much biography can be highly selective. We can conveniently forget the tedium and sheer hard work that brought us to the present. Perhaps this is just as well. September is the month that many people associate with the resumption of the working rhythm of the year. Back to school or back to college after a summer of indolence, or time spent earning money for the next student year.

For us medical students, our third year marked the end of all that. The long holidays were to be a thing of the past. However insignificant we were in the hospital scheme of things, we were part of a team. True we were the least important part, but your absence would be noted, in so far as somebody else would have to do the scut work.

As an example of such vital work carried out by the student corps was the task of transmitting large containers containing 24 or 48-hour collections of stool (faeces) from the wards of the Mater to the laboratories of UCD across the city. The specimens would be tested there for evidence of malabsorption of nutrients from the intestine. In the text books, such motions were described as "pale, bulky and offensive". This was certainly economical with the truth. Few fellow students were willing to accompany the bearer of this burden. A lift in somebody's car was out of the question, and the containers were too unwieldy to be transported by bicycle. The unfortunate future doctor had to resort to public transport. Bus queues melted away as by magic, and very often the unfortunate students found themselves sitting alone on one of the bus decks, even in rush hour. I proposed at one stage they should be given a bell like the lepers of old to warn the populace of their approach. This suggestion was not well received. I am certain, however, that some of the students involved were saved from assault only by the reluctance of the angry citizenry to come to close quarters.

Like any group of young people, our activities were disparate, but our little group based much of our social lives on Hartigan's pub in Leeson Street, known to this day as Harto's, the haunt of medical students (male only then), and the UCD rugby club. I remember my parents being singularly unimpressed some years later, when one of the congratulatory telegrams at my wedding stated simply "Ad Multos Annos Hartos".

We gravitated there at weekends to the very centre of the universe and sallied forth from there looking for parties in flat land. We were a freemasonry and looked after one another. Romances were infrequent, and those involved objects of curiosity. Entertaining ladies other than to the prescribed dress dances was frowned upon and a student who preferred women to beer was held highly suspect. Talking about such things, however, was a different matter and a casual listener might have thought that he had fallen in with a most dissolute group. By and large, the lady students and most certainly our own classmates knew us for the posturing cowardly lot we were.

Time passed pleasantly enough and our resident year drew to a close. An ever intruding thought now was that we had only two years to our finals. Furthermore, there were subjects other than medicine and surgery that we had not yet encountered. Some were very minor and I seem to remember that a cheque through a certain letter box in Fitzwilliam Square produced for all of us a certificate of competence in some minor subject such as leech breeding.

There were serious, hard modules ahead - paediatrics (children), obstetrics and gynaecology (midder). We also had to acquire some knowledge of eyes and ears, of infectious diseases, and of psychiatry. Even the most relaxed among us realised that things were about to change. Only 24 months for all of this while increasing our knowledge base in medicine and surgery. The truth, of course, but not appreciated by us at the time, is that of all the professions, medicine demands life-unceasing learning. These years prepared us well. We accepted without demur that the art came first and that we would build our lives around it.

September 21st, 2004

End is nigh

Retracing my own steps through medical life, I had reached my final year and was heading into final exams. Armageddon was at hand, judgment day had nothing on this. After all, what's a little fire and brimstone compared to telling your parents that you had failed? Or facing the world as a self-designated pariah, knowing that everybody was pointing at you and whispering behind your back? Meanwhile, I will spare you clichés and quotations about time, save to say that it just disappeared. All of us cowards died a thousand times, contemplating the inevitable. I am sure we had at least one brave soul prepared to die but once, but if so I never met him.

The trials grew closer, but there were purification rituals to be undertaken. Foremost among these was the acquisition of the examination suit. I don't think the problem was as acute for the girls, as they seemed used to such rituals and may even have enjoyed them. The essence of this, of course, for parents and guardians was to make sure that their prospective doctor did not appear before his peers lightly disguised as a tramp. Very commendable and, of course, sound common sense, but the recipients of such altruism behaved as if we were being tortured to death. "What do you mean, have a fitting? Don't you realise the exam is only three weeks away? Yes, I fully understand that I can't appear in my pelt." It was a losing battle as us little dears were unwillingly spruced up.

Our hospital tutors in medicine and surgery, kind of demi-gods, midway between celestial consultants and earth-bound NCHDs, tried their utmost to whip us into acceptable shape. We were not to let them or the hospital down. If we let ourselves down, that was our problem. The tutors were like ring masters trying to threaten or cajole their unruly charges into something approaching respectability on the big day.

Great thanks were due to them, they were not too far removed from the ordeal themselves, to be unable to understand how we felt. Their own professional development required intensive study for higher degrees. I have always found that such people make the best teachers.

Another thing that struck us forcibly was that there were "no atheists in foxholes". This phrase, apparently attributed to Lt-Col William J Clear in the last weeks of Bataan, summed up the burst of religious fervour that struck us in the last few weeks. The way of righteousness was to be ours forever, if only the Lord could see his way to doing us a small favour over the next few weeks. For all I know there may even have been some Faustian bargains also - I seem to remember a distinct whiff of sulphur from one individual. In the real world, the Lord helps those who help themselves. The freemasonry of Irish medical students and NCHDs sprang into life. No matter the university or medical school, we were all brothers.

Information began to trickle in about 'interesting' patients in various hospitals. One even heard of patients being kept in hospital for the exams. Could it happen today? We kept lists of what might be encountered and where. We did not know of course where we would be examined, but the word would be passed that a certain hospital was on for the exams on the following day. Various clandestine meetings, usually in pubs, took place nightly and the information was passed on. It must have been our only experience of being teetotal in pubs throughout our student days. On receipt of the lists we went back to our caverns.

Were there any conditions there that you might not know about? Were there any traps, e.g. heart on the wrong side? Were there any difficult or unco-operative patients? Usually there were no surprises, just the conditions, ailments and diseases that we had been learning about. Had we learned enough?

With the nucleus of our own class we now noted grizzled elders who had appeared before and had failed to satisfy the examiners. Their war stories were unsettling, painting a gloomy scenario of an arbitrary process, in which the good were often wronged. Coleridge came to mind, they were best avoided, "by thy long grey beard and glittering eye now wherefore thou stopp'st me?" We had troubles of our own.

Lastly, to say a word about the patients. Generations of Irish doctors owe an enormous debt to the patients who stoically endured us as students. I often felt that to be a patient with an interesting condition or physical sign in hospital, particularly at exam times, required patience and understanding of heroic proportions. Doubtless some refused but most participated willingly, appreciating that their help was essential to our training. I hope that we also learned not only the medicine, but the need to repay their trust with humility and understanding. From us students, to you all - thank you.

Finally on a beautiful June day the waiting was over and on our D-Day we headed for the beaches.

Distilled almost to jelly, by the act of fear - (Hamlet).

November 23rd, 2004

Passing out parade

I have almost finished the journey of my medical student years, albeit a much shortened version. Having written final papers, we now presented ourselves for clinical and oral exams. Scrubbed and shining and in every way unrecognisable, resplendent in our new suits, we arrived at the relevant hospitals for the final chapter. In theory, this was not supposed to be your training hospital, but in practice this sometimes happened and was felt to be a good omen. Through the student underground, we also had a fair idea of the kind of clinical conditions we might encounter.

Thus it was for me that I found myself in the Coombe Hospital for my clinic in obstetrics. A brisk, efficient invigilator allocated me a patient in a numbered cubicle curtained off from the ward. My patient had a breech presentation of her baby, and was also diabetic, requiring insulin. This was a lot to be going on with, but thankfully that was all. She was also able to tell me that her baby hadn't turned around during the night. This provided a certain comfort for the physical examination.

In no time at all, the curtains parted and two examiners commenced to ask me all about the patient. The good lady herself gave me a wink and a broad smile as I went to work. In the afternoon, for the oral exam I drew the external examiner and a local professor. Two more courteous and pleasant men one could not hope to meet, and it was with disbelief afterwards that I realised that I had been with them for over an hour. I had no bad feelings after the day and, if not exactly confident, now faced medicine and surgery with less anxiety.

Medicine, in the now St James's Hospital, provided me with a patient with heart failure caused by a leaking heart valve (shades of the future!). Two brisk no nonsense examiners with straightforward questions required straight answers. The afternoon again provided me with the external examiner and a much-feared local physician. It was a very wide-ranging exam and I recall at one stage it touched on malaria. At the end of the day, I was relieved and felt that I was still upright.

Only surgery to go, and this time I had a problem. I drew the patient from hell. She was a seriously obese and taciturn woman, whose diagnosis of chronic gall-bladder disease had to be extracted slowly and painfully. To compound the problem for me was that she had almost no physical signs. I had two understanding examiners, who realised my difficulties. They pointed out to me that patients like this would be part of my working life. In the afternoon, I completed a full house of external examiners, in a searching and lengthy exam. Then: "Thank you very much, Mr Neligan, I think that is all." That's all, that's it? The exam is over and seven years of my life as a medical student were hopefully behind me.

The results were due the following day. They would initially be read out in the main hall in Earlsfort Terrace, and then posted on the examination boards. Nothing to do now but wait. We began to share our experiences. One unfortunate was asked by the examiner to demonstrate the knee jerk on his patient. His trembling hand succeeded in landing the hammer on the patient's shin, whereupon the patient and examiner winced. A second attempt landed on the patient's groin.

There was a feeling of anticlimax, and of being somehow lost. We wanted to celebrate, but we dared not antagonise the gods. A relatively quiet night and we slept the sleep of the exhausted. Into town in the late morning to meet classmates, a few quiet pints, and a long walk. Then it was time and our silent little group walked the few yards from Hartigans to the Terrace. On time, the dean of the faculty appeared and read out the results. I was a doctor.

The working telephones in the vicinity were besieged. We returned to Hartigans with alacrity, and let our hair down unreservedly. A late migration to Alfredo's in St Mary's Abbey. Remember that anybody? Bed, I presume at some stage. I awoke in the morning regretting the grain and the grape, but facing with excitement and anticipation my changed world.

December 7th, 2004

The first casualty

After the results of our final medical exams became known, we spent a brief period in some sort of Limbo. We were waiting to start our first jobs as qualified doctors. For our group getting an appointment was not all that difficult. Ours was a small medical class, and by the time our overseas classmates had departed, the remainder filled the intern requirements of our teaching hospitals, the Mater and St Vincent's. It was a parting of the ways, because apart from our conferring, we were never together as a group again.

The accepted protocol was that you approached the consultant for whom you wished to work and asked to be considered for the position of House Surgeon or House Physician. If they thought you suitable they would represent you at a meeting of the hospital medical board and shortly thereafter a list of appointees was posted.

We also had to insure ourselves against any havoc we might wreak. There were then basically two organisations providing such medical insurance, both British-based. They were the Medical Defence Union (MDU), and the Medical Protection Society, (MPS). The cost of cover, even to the impecunious newly-qualified, was negligible.

This was to change drastically over the years and the costs now are a fair way into crippling the practice of medicine in many specialities, especially the high-risk ones like obstetrics, neurosurgery, plastic surgery, cardiac surgery and soon. Increasing litigation has led to enormous increases in the cost of delivering medical care, forcing doctors and hospitals to practise defensively.

These nightmares lay in the future and for us it was the toss of a coin as to which organisation you joined. For me fortuitously it was the MPS. Fortuitous indeed considering the problems that have arisen for some doctors insured with the MDU for whom major problems have arisen since the introduction unilaterally by the Department of Health of so-called Enterprise Liability. This indeed may be one of the factors precipitating unprecedented industrial action by doctors in the near future.

There was for us, little time between completing our exams and starting work. No trips to the Far East, Australia or the US were contemplated. In fact by the time we had sorted out our problems, we were left with approximately one week for holiday. Does anybody remember the Amethyst Hotel in Achill Island? I have the fondest memory of the week spent there with some classmates before we joined the real world.

Quiet in late June, we spent our time there, swimming, sunbathing, carousing and above all talking to one another, wondering what the future held. The week passed quickly. It was also the first time that we could say truthfully to the girls, "I am a doctor". I don't think that magic phrase greatly altered outcomes. All too quickly, we headed back to Dublin to begin a new life. I well remember the excitement, the anticipation, and the hopes of being equal to the task.

We did not approach lightly, but seriously and with some foreboding. By this time I knew that my first six months were to be spent as house surgeon to Prof Eoin O'Malley on the surgical professorial team. My second six months were to be spent with Prof Tim Counihan on the medical professorial team. Cardiology and cardiac surgery figured large in both units and the example and encouragement of these outstanding men ultimately led me down my chosen career path.

Shortly before the fateful day, I was approached by one of the previous year's interns, who enquired if I and a couple of my fellows would contemplate starting one day early, as the interns en masse wished to spend their last day together at the Irish Derby at the Curragh. This conversation took place in Hartigan's pub and believe it or not I agreed and furthermore had no trouble in recruiting two colleagues to accompany me.

Thus it was that on that Sunday morning, June 30th, I walked across the threshold of the Mater Hospital to begin my medical career. It was an entirely different experience to that of being there as a student. Now with one wave of the wand, you were right in the firing line, expected to initiate the problems of diagnosis and treatment, and to respond to situations not previously experienced.

We were met by some of our predecessors who gave us the briefest possible idea of our duties and then vanished like smoke. Not for us the luxury of orientation days, it was straight in, at the deep end.

The three volunteers were left to decide who would cover the surgical side, the medical side, and A&E (casualty) department. At that time the Mater had almost as many beds as today but we did not guess what lay ahead.

Firstly we had to present ourselves to the good nun Sr M Rosarii, who was in charge of the residence. Who were we? Why were we a day early? Did we realise we were screwing up the routine? So much for our altruism. We were told the rules and allotted our monastic cells, bed, inbuilt wardrobe, and multi-purpose sink. We had first choice of rooms, upstairs in the residence, away from the common room and the flight path of returning revellers at night.

There was also an area called the Espiello, where the lady doctors were housed. The many statues in the residence were also put to bed there on party nights. It was a year before it was pointed out to us that the correct appellation of the harem was SPLO (Strictly Private, Ladies Only). While placing my belongings in the room there came a knock, "Doctor you are wanted in casualty". A new life had begun.

We've only 40 more years to go. Do you think we'll all last the pace?

January 18th, 2005

The other side of the divide

There is a voluminous literature on the doctor-patient relationship. Some would maintain that even more is written about its absence. Thankfully I have only once been a patient and when I was, I was a bad one. I do not propose to dwell on this in the hope that those caring for me then will have forgotten about it.

I will, however, talk about how it was for me on the other side of the divide. There were no meaningful textbooks or primers on how to relate to patients. Observation and instruction by our teachers had contributed much, but at the end of the day the individual doctors and patients defined their own relationships.

As an intern you were the first port of call. You took the initial comprehensive history, including previous medical history, family history and social history, and anything else relevant. Sometimes the history was delivered by a wife, acting as if the husband was not there or was bereft of the power of speech. In this latter instance it was usually accompanied by observations like "He drinks/smokes too much. He never takes any exercise."

En passant, is it any wonder that the women live longer? The initial history, examination and ordering of tests seldom took less than three-quarters of an hour. On a busy unit with many admissions this made for a very long day. Relatively minor complaints and injuries could be processed fairly quickly, but on the other hand very sick and complicated patients took a long time, and we were only learning.

In student days we took histories and examined patients. Now we did the same, but now they were our patients and we had to get to know them. We were between them and the physicians and surgeons who were in charge. We hopefully learned, as Edward Goodman said: "It is a distinct art to talk medicine in the language of the non-medical man." Maybe this was the development of a bedside manner. We learned also to avoid wherever possible the pitfalls for the unwary.

I found that about 10 per cent of patients gave a straightforward, unambiguous description of their condition. A further 40 per cent gave a totally inadequate history, some because they were incapable of so doing, some suppressing salient points through fear. In this group came the frankly uncommunicative patients and the smart ones: "What's the matter?" "That's your job to find out."

About another 40 per cent were garrulous, often in the extreme, and the path to diagnosis was strewn with red herrings and marked by culs de sac and diversions. Hypochondriacs belonged here, if there was indeed a nugget of illness buried in the verbiage you had to dig deep to find it. This often required more patience than we possessed. In the final 10 per cent, the history was provided by paramedics or relatives, with treatment coming first and history coming later.

We learned, as Sir William Jenner pointed out: "Never believe what a patient tells you his doctor has said." We learned to deal with exaggeration and suppression and we learned how to recognise and be gentle with fear. We found it less easy to deal with anger. Fear, helplessness and uncertainty made some patients, and indeed relatives, angry.

"In time we hate that which we so often fear." (Anthony and Cleopatra.)

Such anger is often vented on the carers and even with understanding of its cause is most difficult to handle. Tired overworked staff have to swallow hard to rationalise abuse and anger. We had been taught and had observed the perils of becoming too closely involved with the trials and terrors that sickness visited on some.

Throughout my career this has proved extremely difficult especially when dealing with children. We had to learn to deal with disappointment, the pain of fearsome diagnosis and the certainty of death. These were difficult tasks for young people and, in hindsight, of course, there were times when you might have done better. You learned also that you did not have rapport with everyone. Not every patient or family liked you. The converse also held true.

Having started in July, the summer just disappeared, we had lots of work and very little play, but we had an increasing appreciation of our role within the hospital. We became used to being called at night and often running through a darkened silent sleeping hospital, and realising that in the first instance you were "the man".

You entertained your doubts and worries and learned all the time. That first August was quiet for me, but things were about to change. A vignette of that August remains with me. I was sitting in the residence on a warm sunny afternoon, reading the paper, the surgical registrar slept in an adjacent chair. The door opened to admit one of my lady fellow interns. The registrar awoke, looked around and said: "There she is Maurice, say it to her face". To this day she does not accept my protestations.

I was removed from the casualty roster, as it was explained to me that I would be first on call for the post-operative heart operations and would be required on those nights to sleep in the intensive care unit, such as it was then. This often followed a very long day in theatre. It was for me the start of my involvement in the branch of surgery that was to become my life. In retrospect, I loved every minute.

March 15th, 2005

Gripped from the outset

Thousands of operations later, it is still not difficult to remember the beginning. I had as an intern become accustomed to the operating theatres and procedures, far more so than as a student. In other words I was no longer scared stiff. I was involved in the preparation of the scene and any deficiencies in preparation would rightly, and occasionally wrongly, be laid at my door. Our team did general surgery as well as chest and heart surgery. Some of the heart surgery did not require the use of the heart-lung machine; eg dilating the mitral valve from outside the heart, and repairing congenital lesion like patent ductus arteriosus and coarctation of the aorta, all of which could be approached through the left chest with the patient lying on the right side.

In later years we came to realise that although the machine was not necessary in these cases, it was very comforting to have it in the background in case things went wrong. Even in the best ordered scheme of things, disasters may occur, and given the nature of the surgery, with sometimes calamitous results.

Open heart surgery was another dimension altogether. In the vast majority of cases the heart was approached from the front and after dividing the skin over the sternum (breast bone), the bone itself was divided longitudinally, right down the middle, using an instrument in those days called a Gigli saw. This in essence was a strong braided wire, with loops on either end. This wire was passed up behind the bone using a very long forceps, and eventually retrieved at the base of the neck. Handles were attached to the loops, and the bone literally sawed through. It sounds crude and it was, but it was effective. Things are somewhat different today but the approach remains the same. The two sides of the bone were separated by a self retaining retractor, ie it did not have to be held in place. This done, the pericardium, (the cover around the heart) was opened and the heart exposed.

Needless to say the patient slept happily(?), during all this time. The drugs required to enable the patient to be connected to the heart-lung machine were given. Tubes (cannulae) were placed in the collecting chamber of the heart on the right side, enabling the blood returning to the heart to be diverted to the machine. Here, the oxygenator part of the machine, removed the carbon dioxide from the blood and added oxygen, as the normal lungs would do. This blood was then returned to the circulation on the arterial side downstream from the heart. This enabled the machine to support the circulation, thus enabling the heart to be stopped and repaired. Sounds easy?

Well, experience made it so, and better machines, tubing, oxygenators, pumps etc made all of this the routine that it is today, but it did not come about without tears. This is not intended to be the Peter and Jane guide to cardiac surgery, but rather to provide a rough if very foggy clue as to what we were about.

As part of the circulation was now outside the body, a volume of blood (later other fluids), was necessary to fill this system. This unsurprisingly was known as the priming volume. The older machines were large and cumbersome and required a large volume. For such operations, it was customary to order 12 units of blood. This could create problems if blood was in short supply or if the patient had an unusual blood group or had blood problems. I will say that in my very extensive surgical experience, we were never let down by the Blood Transfusion Service, which always, even in the most desperate of circumstances, seemed to somehow manage. This despite the fact that like the rest of the health system, they were under-funded and under-staffed.

At this time they managed to do without me participating in the actual surgery. My job was that of a "gofer" doing the routine work on the wards and being available to the operating team if required. Occasionally you might be required to scrub-up and participate, usually just to hold something. Despite the fact that you were certain that you had much to contribute, even at that fledgling stage, you were in fact wiser to keep your mouth shut and your opinions to yourself.

The lead surgeon often had problems of his own and the inanities uttered by the most junior member of the team were rarely welcomed. I believe this is called "learning your place". I always had difficulty with this concept. I watched, I listened, I learned, and personally I was fascinated. From those magic early days, I wanted nothing other than to be a cardiac surgeon, a career choice I have never regretted.

Many of the patients of the time were extremely sick and had been deteriorating steadily over the years, waiting Micawber-like for something to turn up. Something as often in medicine did turn up, but sadly for some it was too late. On their misfortune grew our experience and such lessons learned in disappointment and failure were often the best remembered and instructive.

I note that things are still happening in the real world. One really good thing is the appointment of Prof Brendan Drumm, a colleague from both Crumlin and Comhairle Na hOspidéal. I have great personal respect for Brendan, and if anybody can make sense of this, he can. However, he cannot do it on his own, and it behoves all who realise the problems to contribute in any helpful way.

April 19th, 2005

Lessons
learnt the hard way

Each morning sees some task begin,
Each evening sees it close;
Something attempted, something done,
Has earned a night's repose.
(Longfellow)

You might have earned the repose, but it seldom worked out that way. I had been recalling my experiences of the hospital at night in my intern days and now I learn that a study of call patterns for NCHDs (junior doctors), and an assessment of what actually happens in a big hospital at night is under way.

It was fairly simple in my day. Your range of calls went from the small, such as resiting an infusion, or getting a consent form signed, to dire emergency calling on all your meagre reserves of knowledge and experience. There were calls for night sedation for patients who could not sleep. The rationale for this seemed to be that if that were not sleeping on the ward then you weren't going to sleep either. There were calls to deal with everything from the DTs to death and as sure as hell you didn't wander round the wards at night just for fun. Calls sometimes came from the private hospital. This was not the impressive Mater Private of today, but rather a collection of interconnected Georgian houses adjoining the main hospital on Eccles Street.

These were not popular calls because if the interconnecting door between the hospital and the private was locked, you had to leave by the main door and make your way down the street and then bang on the door to gain admission. The weather was no better then and wet cold and miserable in the small hours, you felt as if the woes of the world were upon you. The said woes did not stop there. Staffing at night was less than in the main hospital and everything was locked, medicine cabinets and equipment stores of all kinds. Trying to organise anything there was difficult and took an inordinate time.

One of the top corridors in the private was reputed to be haunted, as indeed was one of the staircases in the main hospital. God knows I suppose enough people perished in odd circumstances in both institutions to make this entirely plausible. I never encountered either restless spirit despite being abroad in the witching hours often enough.

It was during this time that we became really aware that patients were essentially divided into two groups. These were called public and private and they were supposed to be different. It wasn't immediately obvious wherein the difference lay, but it existed.

It was more discernible in the female of the species. They often let you know that they clearly understood the menial place you occupied in the grand scheme of things. They were quick to complain and more demanding of service. Sometimes we interns felt that the level of hypochondriasis in this group was above average and the tolerance of minor discomfort was way below average. Any opinions you held on this interesting social phenomenon, if you were wise you kept to yourself.

There were a lot of religious in this elite group. I well remember a colleague, who although not on duty, was deputed by his boss to look after an eminent cleric who had undergone a prostatectomy that morning. This was not an operation that generally gave a lot of trouble post-operatively and our colleague was incensed at being told, not asked, to give up his time off to look after the eminent patient. He made these points eloquently to the rest of us, who having listened sympathetically, urged him to go and tell his boss what to do. The coward did not take our advice and thus preserved his career. He moped around the residence all evening, occasionally checking the entirely stable patient in the private hospital.

Eventually the lure of the bright lights of Hartigan's pub in Leeson Street grew irresistible and having briefed his cover and the nurse in charge, and leaving Hartigan's telephone number he decamped to join his fellows.

At 10.30 he was called to the phone in the noisy bar and found he was talking to his consultant. How was bishop X? He is very well sir. Pulse and blood pressure are all right? They are normal sir. Is the urinary catheter draining freely? Yes sir. There is no bleeding? No sir. At this stage a freezing blast of air emanated from the earpiece of the phone. I don't know where you are doctor Y, but I am here with the bishop and the resuscitation team. The bishop has no pulse or blood pressure, the catheter is blocked and the drip is not running. You had better present yourself forthwith. Sheer panic, pint abandoned, run to Shelbourne, taxi to Mater career in ruins. Dear Jesus what do I do? Think of an excuse. In the door of the Private run three flights of stairs, night nurse looking at him curiously. What's happening, he gasped? Nothing she said, the bishop has been stable all evening. Mr Consultant rang just after you left and I gave him the number you left. We learned at all levels and as Tacitus put it "Experientia docuit".

Nursing home problems arise, why am I not surprised? Bet you anything nobody is responsible.

June 7th, 2005

163

Length does matter

The Leaving Certificate results have just been released, bringing their usual share of happiness and grief. For those students who have the points to do medicine, I have the temerity to offer some advice. Think hard before you commit. It is a vocation and you will not be truly happy unless you really want to be a doctor. If you do, then come and join us and feel welcome in this most satisfying of careers. I know we all complain a lot and things are not always as they should be. Perhaps in your future professional life you can make a difference. You must always so believe.

Thinking of the pathways in medical life returns me to my own. I was in my surgical internship in the Mater and was beginning to feel I had been there all my life. I had become used to low pay and anti-social hours and had become brainwashed to expect nothing else. I had not become used to the ever-changing patterns of illness and disease and to the medical responses. The fascination gripped early and thankfully it never left.

Quite early in our internship our little group began to evince interests in the various branches of the profession. More inclined towards the medical as opposed to the surgical side; slowly, hesitantly, career paths were being chosen. Reality intervened here, and mentors and colleagues sometimes pointed out the pitfalls along the way and maybe ever so gently queried the suitability of the aspirant for the path they had selected. The wise heeded the advice.

The putative surgeons and, I suppose, I would have to include those strange folk whose interest lay in obstetrics and gynaecology, began to spend as much time as possible in the operating theatres and their environs. Assisting at surgery was the thing to do, where you began to learn the craft, and where you found if your heart and hands were up for the job. This, bearing in mind the aphorism of Alexandre Dumas Snr that "a good surgeon operates with his hand, not with his heart". This is undoubtedly true in the individual case, but in the generality the heart must be involved in the commitment to the surgical life.

From student days we had learned to stitch cuts. Now we learned to sew up surgical incisions and set simple fractures, albeit under strict supervision. This ranged from the consultant to the registrar to the operating room nurse, the latter usually being the most severe critic. I must not forget the anaesthetists who frequently hissed at you if you had been left to close a wound on your own. "Hurry up for Christ's sake, do you want to keep us here all day?"

We were expected to move quickly and were beginning to learn that, as Russell Howard put it, "speed in operating should be the achievement, not the aim, of every surgeon". We learned to tie surgical knots, and the backs of chairs, handles of drawers and indeed door knobs became festooned with our efforts. We read the basics of surgical handicraft and operating techniques and imperceptibly and invidiously surgery began to possess our souls.

Accordingly, it was with mixed feelings for the rest of us when a colleague said smugly at breakfast one morning: "I did an appendix last night; Joe [the registrar] took me through it."

The stakes were raised and thereafter the registrars on emergency call were haunted. Acute appendicitis became a very important diagnosis for us tyro surgeons as we waited our chance to do our first real operation. For those of you reading this who have had their appendix removed in a general hospital, you may have been somebody's first operation. There comes a time when every bird flies for the first time, thus it is with surgeons. Yes, you are supervised but you hold the knife. We had the surgical registrars damned to find suitable cases with which to launch our careers and, finally, on a rainy Friday night in November my moment came. The patient was an 18-year-old boy with the classical signs and symptoms of acute appendicitis. Theatre was arranged and I was on my way. I would lie to you if I said that scrubbing up, gowning and painting and draping the patient was the same as always. Things are always different when you are doing them yourself.

My stage was set, grumpy anaesthetist, grumpy nurses, united on a common grump of "Jesus, he's not going to let the intern do it, we'll be here all night." The relaxed registrar was the epitome of calm efficiency. Wherever you are Gerry, thanks. Knife to skin, gentle pressure, little bleeding, separate rather than cut muscle layers, open the peritoneum - the membrane that envelops the abdominal organs. Hook a finger inside and extract the small bowel, check for a rarity called Meckel's diverticulum. Follow the small bowel down to where it joins the colon, and there, Eureka, a large fat inflamed appendix. Totally engrossed yet moving quickly, appendix removed and wound sewn up. Out of there realising that I was a changed man.

If you had your appendix out in the Mater hospital in November 1962 and have a neat one and a half inch scar, you may have been my first surgical case. On the other hand, if you have a scar about 10 inches long that looks as if it was sewn up with baler twine, it must have been one of my colleagues. This is one of the rare instances when men think one and a half inches is preferable to 10 inches any time. It was then back to earth with a bang to the ordinary humdrum life of an intern. But deep down something had changed.

August 23rd, 2005

Finding the right direction

Writing about the health service is like writing about the Middle East. A lot happens, but seldom anything good. The preservation of my sanity precludes the endless cataloguing of failure and incompetence in this most fundamental area and, accordingly, I promise not to refer to it again in this article. Such resolution allows me to return to days gone by and my own little story. I had last written about my days as a medical intern in the Mater and there I shall resume.

As the spring of my intern year turned into summer, our routine professional life, and what passed as our social life, continued as before. We had acquired some confidence, albeit easily bruised, and generally felt we were becoming better doctors, a dangerous place to be indeed. Everything was no longer a mountain to be climbed and initial fears and even enthusiasms had been dulled by routine, interspersed as it was by occasional drama. We lived in our own little comfort zone and responded with varying alacrity to the rhythms of hospital life.

In a way it was too comfortable to last and it did not. The lengthening of the days meant the shortening of our intern year and the intrusion of thoughts of the future into our comfortable present. Thinking of our lives and futures had been suspended in our world of life, sickness and death. Now we had to think of what lay ahead. Such thoughts had come unbidden, like dreams, on many occasions, but now became persistent and for even the most light-hearted of us, serious. "The thoughts of youth are long, long thoughts" (Longfellow) and so they were. What were we to do with the rest of our professional lives? Were the career paths that we hoped for, feasible? How long would future training take, and were there job opportunities in that particular field? Should we at this early stage of professional development be looking at the particular or should we seek more experience in the general?

The questions were myriad and, to us, the permutations and combinations of answers were but slowly grasped. Some generalities were obvious. There was broadly a choice between hospital medicine and general practice. In hospital life there were multiple areas: medicine, surgery, obstetrics, pathology, radiology, anaesthetics, etc. Did any of these appeal?

How did you go about taking your first steps in your chosen direction? Nowadays, once the choice is made, the route to attainment is made clearer and more straightforward. Training schemes exist in nearly all medical disciplines and, in theory at least, once you set foot on your chosen pathway, you should at the end of your journey be fully qualified to take your place as an independent practitioner. The latter in no way precludes team working in specialist groupings. There is now also better application of training needs to future requirements in the service, although in many disciplines there is still a considerable way to go.

In my days such structured support was simply non-existent, and much individual advice and help had to be sought as to how best achieve the required training. The past and present, however, shared one inescapable fact. It was still up to the individual young doctor to decide what he or she wanted to do.

Such a decision was among the most important of your life. A mixture of motives and vocations came into play here. Can I make money? Will I have to get up at night? Can I have a "normal" social life? My daddy is one already and the door is open. I would like to help people. I find the work fascinating. Will I have to go away for training, or for ever? Some decided early and pressed on boldly, some required several false starts before they settled, an unfortunate few never settled at all. In theory as Propertius put it in the century before the birth of Christ: "let each man pass his days in that wherein his skill is greatest". Ah, quite so, but we had to find out and acknowledge, sometimes painfully, where our skills and aptitude lay and furthermore was there to be an available arena in which to display them.

There was also the uncomfortable feeling that our own assessment of our aptitudes and capabilities might not be shared by those crucial to our professional development. There was also the problem that the initial fire of certainty and enthusiasm might well be quenched in the cold world of reality. In truth, the future was clear cut for few, and most of us were launching our craft into a sea of uncertainty.

Most of us entertained such thoughts only briefly, and the implications noted and dismissed, on the grounds that the world was our oyster and that it would be all right on the night. I knew even then what I wanted to do. I wanted to be a cardio-thoracic surgeon. It was a rapidly expanding specialty and I reasoned that it would offer great challenges and opportunities in the not too distant future here in Ireland. That for me, as for most Irish people, was very important. But you must learn to walk before you can run and accordingly, I would first have to train and qualify as a general surgeon and then if the lights were still green, proceed on the specialist road I had chosen.

Years more hospital work, training and exams lay ahead but I looked forward to that, attracted as I was to the surgical, and indeed hospital life. It was imminent and in the meantime I could revert to my boy scout days and refresh my ability to tie knots.

February 14th, 2006

Dying is not that easy

Mortality weighs heavily on me, like unwilling sleep
(John Keats)

That's a gloomy start and to accentuate the feeling of despondency, it is a uniformly grey day and it has been raining all morning. The cause of my lowered spirits was the news of the death of a friend and colleague who at one stage was the other half of our complement of two surgical registrars in the Mater. I wish my friends would stop dying; it is quite unsettling and me only in the prime of life. Have you noticed how the prime of life seems to stretch toward the horizon like a rainbow's end as you advance in age? I remember a colleague asking us all in exasperation, after dealing with the very concerned family of a senior citizen: "Who would want to live to 94?" The answer, of course, is anybody of 93.

Gerry had been a great colleague, an ideal one, as you made your first faltering passes with the knife. He was completing his term when I arrived and was a rock of sense with a leavening of experience. Placed just above me on the surgical ladder, he helped me climb in the best tradition of surgical training. I remember asking him on one occasion why he had decided upon a surgical career. He told me that he had been inspired by Mr Hackancut. I looked aghast at him. "He's the worst surgeon I know," I protested. "I accept that," he replied patiently, "but I reckon that if he can make a good living from surgery, then anybody can!" Gerry went on to become a plastic surgeon of great repute in the United States but always kept in touch with us at home. God be with you now Gerry in a place where your considerable skills are now presumably redundant.

It strikes me that notwithstanding the huge changes over the centuries in the practice of surgery, one thing has remained constant. That is the sure conviction that as young apprentice surgeons we could operate more skilfully than our clumsy seniors. The trick was not to show this too obviously, as it could have career-ending consequences. It was only to be shared with fellow tyros usually in circumstances where tongues were loosened by drink. Even in such circumstances you had to be careful. The whistleblowers (informers) were always among us and a snide remark to the consultant like, "Mr Neligan thinks you couldn't cut your way out of a paper bag" could also have a deleterious effect on your prospects.

The tinted glass of remembrance leaves mostly good memories. The times you erred and had to be bailed out existed but you consciously suppress such recollections and console yourself by thinking they must have been few enough. It was not a career pathway that could be delineated by disasters. One certain thing from early days and throughout a surgical life; I was never bored. Tired, bad-tempered at times, scared witless at others, feelings of helplessness and inadequacy, all these were part of the continuous process of learning the art. Ennui was not.

Every passing day brought a little more of that invaluable commodity, experience. Surgery could not be learned from books alone, important as they were in our foundation. Instead observation, assisting and then operating with supervision, then without, is the via dolorosa of the surgical trainee. Sir Astley Cooper, one of the great anatomists and early surgeons, wrote: "I have made many mistakes myself; in learning the anatomy of the eye I dare say I have spoiled a hatful; the best surgeon like best general is he who makes the fewest mistakes." Mind you, the same surgeon also wrote: "My lectures are highly esteemed, but I am of the opinion that my operations rather kept down my practice." We live and lived in more accountable times.

Illustrative of the continual change in medical practice is the story of the treatment of peptic ulceration. As a surgical registrar scarcely a general surgical operating list did not feature patients with this condition undergoing one or other of the myriad operations devised for its relief. It was held that hyper secretion of acid (HCl) was the primary causative agent and many of the surgical procedures addressed this fallacy. We now know that this condition is largely caused by an infection with an organism, H. Pylorii, so it is hardly surprising that the surgical results were disappointing. Indeed it is almost axiomatic that if many operations are devised for a condition, it is usually because none of them gives uniform satisfaction.

The complications of such ulcers, notably perforation and bleeding, took up a goodly part of our early emergency work. My diary records three such operations seriatim from 10pm on Christmas Eve to 4am on Christmas morning. No sympathy from the consultant; in surgical parlance, I was learning my way around the abdomen. The discovery of the causative organism and its successful treatment meant that many of these operations have followed bleeding, cupping and the leech into oblivion.

The consultant surgeons then had no contracts, no 33-hour week. Honoré de Balzac wrote of the earlier generations: "The glory of surgeons is like that of actors, who exist only in their lifetime and whose talent is no longer appreciated after they have disappeared."

Most who I have been privileged to know would wish it no other way.

October 31st, 2006

Trouble buzzed around

Writing in a previous column about surgical training and trainers retuned my thoughts to times past. I know this is a family newspaper but I cannot but include this salutary story from my registrar years.

My consultant at the time, Mr X, appeared one morning in theatre in extremely good humour. He told us that he had been at a largely medical dinner party on the previous evening and had met a GP who told him about a patient with a most unusual problem. Apparently the patient, a youngish man, was in the habit of walking around with his finger inserted in his rear end. This somewhat disconcerted his family who sent him to the luckless GP. The history given was that a bee had somehow gained admission to these parts and the buzzing, particularly at night, the patient avowed, was driving him out of his mind. The doctor avoided the temptation of observing that such would be a short journey. Instead, after an unrewarding physical examination, he reasoned with the patient and stressed the implausibility of such an event. It was all to no avail and sedation and purgatives were no help. Nothing could shift the bee, the fixation or indeed the finger.

173

Treading carefully with a now disgruntled patient, who felt that he was not being taken seriously, he managed to arrange a psychiatric consultation. No joy there. The patient disclaimed any history of bee stings or even that he had been sexually molested by a bee in his childhood. It was at this stage that my boss became involved. Some might have doubted the wisdom of this, as surgeons traditionally are held to be more doers than thinkers. This of course is pejorative nonsense as my man was about to prove. He positively beamed as he told us his postulated solution. In short, a very light quick anaesthetic for the patient, who on coming around, would be simply told that the bee had been removed. "What do you think of that?" he asked. Not much we all felt, but fear of lese-majeste rendered us cravenly quiet.

The day dawned and the procedure was undertaken, the anaesthetist also expressing grave doubts about its efficacy. Mr X then played his trump card. From a pocket he produced a glass jar containing a large indignant bumble bee culled from his garden earlier that morning. Despite ourselves we were impressed, but not half as much as the patient apparently; "God bless you Mr X. I knew all along that I was right. They were trying to make out that I was mad." "Not at all," said Mr X smoothly, "but luckily for you I had a similar case before and knew exactly what to do." The patient was discharged, elated and cured. As Mr X was never one to hide his light under a bush, the story spread like wildfire. The gist of the expected response was to be the acknowledgement of what a wily cunning clever old bird he was.

The Ancient Mariner had nothing on him and we heard the story repeatedly over the next few weeks, (the Highest Authority maintains that I have a tendency to repeat my stories, but this of course is quite untrue). The saga came to an abrupt end at the next out-patient clinic. The patient was noted to be wriggling around uncomfortably and indeed on being brought to the cubicle for examination it was found that he had reinserted his finger. Mr X was incandescent. "Don't tell me there's another ******* bee up there," he roared. "Oh no" Mr X, came the reply, "but you did such a great job curing me, that I'm making sure one can't get up there again." Since then, we never heard the story again.

Each day seemed to bring something new then. You learned something or you did something for the first time and gradually you became competent. I am thinking about the deep fear that you might have if you felt that you had unwittingly harmed a patient. The "registrar's test - cut it and see what happens" was meant as a joke. We didn't find it very funny.

Years of anatomy stood us in good stead. Anatomical variations were not uncommon when nerves, veins or arteries were not where they were meant to be, or where they divided and branched unexpectedly. Experience made you less bothered by this but there were times when the wisest course was to down tools and send for help. It was always there.

Re-operations were always a cause for concern. Crudely put, everything was often stuck from the previous operation, ie there were multiple adhesions. The tissue planes and normal anatomical landmarks were often obscured and festina lente was the rule. Dense fibrous scar tissue had to be dissected away, millimetre by millimetre and yet in a manner that kept the operation moving forward in a seemingly unhurried fashion. A truism early taught was that for best results you had to have good exposure of the area being operated upon and that you must have control of any major blood vessels therein.

Sounds easy doesn't it? Well it wasn't always, and this is where previous surgery and obese patients caused problems. It was not that you were likely to sever something inappropriate but a nick in an artery or vein could cause serious bleeding and obscure the field of operation. It was one thing to anticipate trouble, it was another to deal with it when it came from a clear blue sky. This happened too.

December 12th, 2006

Restoring common sense

When writing about sports injuries recently, an incident from my registrar days in the Mater hospital came to mind. When the Dominican Convent and school in Eccles Street closed and was purchased by the Mater, we acquired a basketball court.

In residence at that time we had a vertically challenged but highly enthusiastic aficionado of the sport. Leslie from Singapore duly obtained several basketballs and cajoled a rather unenthusiastic bunch of residents to participate. Initially our efforts resembled a cross between Gaelic football and rugby, with a very slight admixture of the game itself. We improved gradually and eventually sought competition from outside. One summer's evening, a team of clerical students from Clonliffe College came to give battle, literally as it turned out, to our team.

It was quickly apparent that there was a gulf in class between the sides. They were taller and fitter than us and one particular gentleman, about 6' 7" in height, was giving us endless grief. A huddle was called and instructions given to Paddy Mac, a surgical intern who had been a Mayo minor footballer, to deal with this menace. Unfortunately, things did not go according to plan and the menace objected most strenuously to being "dealt with". A most unsavoury brawl developed when it became apparent that these aspiring pillars of the Church had no intention of meekly turning the other cheek.

Eventually order was restored and the game, our first and last against outside opposition, ended in total defeat. I wondered afterwards if the authorities in Clonliffe did not think it slightly unusual that two of their seminarians should sport major black eyes after a basketball match. I suppose it had something to do with the "church militant".

I, however, had my own problems. Towards the end of this debacle I hurt my back and had to be assisted to our A&E department by the few spectators present. There I received little sympathy, the senior staff nurse opining that I should have more sense and the good nun in charge concurring in this belief. Two aspirins, a pair of crutches and a total absence of tender loving care. I was the surgical registrar on call and I could only pray that a quiet night lay ahead. God let me down, doubtless because of the earlier fracas.

That same evening, one Richard Rock was returning to Dublin from some musical triumph abroad and was met at the airport by a delighted throng of appreciative fans. In the midst of the "spit on me Dickie" delirium, a balcony collapsed and many were returned to earth with a bump. The hospital was notified of a major emergency and ambulances full of hysterical victims arrived on our doorstep. The department was in Shakespearean parlance, "full of sound and fury; signifying nothing". The surgical registrar facing this screaming avalanche was so far gone in self pity that he considered himself in more pain than any of those being assessed and treated. I might also note that those afflicted got far more sympathy than their treating doctor had, some hours previously.

The arrival of a real "acute abdomen" delivered me from this hysterical Hades, and it was almost a relief, crutches, pain and all, to escape to the calm of the operating theatre. That night left me with an aversion to white sport coats and pink carnations and chapels on the hill, and also to the game of basketball.

177

Sometimes, despite the best efforts of Sr M Rosarii, who looked after us waifs in residence so well, we would augment our diet by dispatching emissaries to the "chipper" just up the road in Phibsboro. Also in this time of Methuselah, a hamburger bar opened at the junction of Eccles Street and Dorset Street offering a change of cuisine to our jaded palates.

Shortly after its opening, my fellow surgical registrar, later a distinguished neurosurgeon in Belfast, drew the short straw to visit this new culinary haven to procure provisions for his starving colleagues. It was a complicated order: 28 hamburgers, some with mustard, some ketchup, some both, x chips and assorted drinks. He duly departed only to return a short time later empty handed.

He had joined the queue at pub-closing time and gradually worked his way to the top. When the magnitude of his order percolated to the gentry behind, a riot nearly ensued and he was told in graphic terms to remove himself. He claimed that the interest of public order rather than intimidation made him withdraw. His prudent stance was not appreciated by his colleagues in the residency either.

I think at the time, Dublin had one or two Indian or Chinese restaurants, and kebabs and pizzas were in the distant future, and yet somehow we survived. I suppose it is a sign of the times that an outbreak of food poisoning allegedly originating in a Sligo town is considered newsworthy. We residents were felled almost yearly by the same condition and never made it to the papers.

No Health and Safety Authority then, no inspections, no closing down of kitchens; such protections lay in a future beyond our imagining. Yet our hospitals functioned and the sick were looked after in dignity and with compassion. Common sense ruled. I wonder where it went. I suppose it wasn't politically correct enough for these times.

September 4th, 2007

Missing out on compliments of the season

I think my memory mirror is slanted to reflect the good times. Most people can suppress the recall of bad days and I am no exception. Writing recently about the medical diaspora set me thinking about my own experiences. As my time of training in the Mater drew to a close, I had been exposed to all the relevant surgical specialities and had crossed the exam hurdles. I had decided that I wanted to be a cardiac surgeon. The speciality was expanding rapidly, with new developments on an almost monthly basis.

Prof Eoin O'Malley, who was heading the fledgling programme in the Mater, encouraged me and told me that he would look for a suitable training opportunity in a good unit in the UK. While waiting, there were now other things in my life; the Highest Authority, then working as an anaesthetic registrar in the Mater, had acquired me and I was now married.

Soon after marriage we had a stroke of luck. The Mater, ahead of its time, developed married quarters for resident registrars near the hospital. We were the first inhabitants of the flat in Geraldine Street, just across Berkeley Road from the hospital. It was a small flat but adequate for two working doctors. At the time I was working for the senior surgeon in the hospital. He was a very pleasant man in the good times, but did not suffer fools gladly and could be irascible.

On Christmas morning, the doorbell rang and on the step was my fellow surgical registrar who was on duty on the day. He came to wish us the compliments of the season. The HA produced mince pies and tea for this overseas newly-arrived doctor who was an accomplished and experienced surgeon. While we were talking the phone rang. A well-known voice bellows in my ear that the superior of a well known religious order was at that moment on his way into the hospital by ambulance and that I was to be there to meet him.

Diffidently, I replied that I was not on duty, but fortuitously Mr Z, who was on duty, was with me and would he like to speak to him? The voice informed me and the whole room that he didn't want that person (he used a different word) going near his patient. I put down the phone and my colleague asked me if that had been the boss, and why was it that he, although on duty, was not to see the patient. Was he not trusted and should he ring the senior surgeon immediately and have it out with him?

Happy Christmas I thought; this I can do without. Lying through my teeth I explained that I had seen the patient before. This feeble explanation was accepted with thinly veiled scepticism. Céad míle fáilte, welcome to the land of fog.

I made my way to a Christmas hospital, complete with crib, lights, streamers and balloons, spotless and tidy with everyone in festive humour. A good sister asked me if I would have a little drop, seeing the day that was in it. Glumly I told her that I was in my way to A&E to see a patient. On arrival in the department, all was quiet. People tend not to get sick on Christmas Day and the unit bore no resemblance to the war zone of Christmas Eve.

The staff had been advised of the imminent arrival and together with the nun in charge we waited and waited and then waited some more. I called the HA and told her to go on without me. That's a surgical anthem known to the brethren worldwide.

Eventually an ambulance drew up, the swing doors parted and a trolley was wheeled in. "Well?" I inquired. "He's dead doc," came the reply. "He was dead when we collected him." Despite the day, there was to be no Lazarus moment. I turned to the nun, "Your province Sister, and I had better ring the chief". I did so and after a brief silence came, "What do you mean he's dead?"

I bit my tongue and explained very politely that the subject fulfilled all the criteria necessary for a diagnosis of death. He then inquired if any of the community had accompanied the deceased. "No", I told him. "You had better wait until somebody turns up," he said and put down the phone. I missed the bit where he said thanks, and sotto voce I wished him a memorable Christmas.

On my way back through a darkening hospital I met the nun who had offered me the drop. "If the offer's still open sister, I'll take you up on it," Christmas starts now.

October 27th, 2009

Remembering loved ones at Christmas time

The national goose is being cooked and there is precious little any of us lesser mortals can do about it. Unfortunately the cook doesn't seem to have much of a clue and God only knows what kind of an unpalatable mess is going to land on our table. Right now I intend to ignore all the problems of the present and retreat into the past. It seems safer there.

My father died on Christmas Day, 30 years ago at four o'clock in the afternoon. Given that we all have to depart some time, he chose to go in an unforgettable manner. My parents had a flat with us in Blackrock and on that morning we had all gone to my sister's house for drinks. He was in fine form, his three children and all his grandchildren were there. He had his few drinks and smoked a few cigarettes and was in the best of form. I might add that he had smoked 40 a day since going to sea in the merchant marine as a young man. He never had the slightest inclination to stop.

He was a fit man for his years (84) and was still driving competently. He also liked a drink with friends, the odd game of cards and he loved to go fishing. He didn't seem the kind of person who would die and certainly I, as his only son, never thought about a time when he might not be around. He was just there, an immovable fixture, deeply loved by us all. As is often the case of course we did not tell him that; it would have made him deeply uncomfortable and he might have wondered had we some ulterior motive, babysitting duties perhaps.

Christmas dinner was scheduled for four o'clock that afternoon and all was in readiness. About half an hour before the start my mother rang from the granny flat to say that he wasn't well and seemed to have severe abdominal pain. I went up to him and found him in extremis . To this day I am not sure if he knew I was there. He tried to slip away quietly but we wouldn't let him. The HA and I tried to resuscitate him and phoned for an ambulance. We knew in our hearts he had left us, but we had to try. God might have made a mistake. In the midst of our efforts our two elder sons appeared to announce that their electronic Christmas present wasn't working. What are you doing to Grandad? Not enough, what could we do, we were helpless.

The paramedics arrived and took my dad away to St Vincent's. They were great guys, strong and sympathetic; indeed this has been my overriding impression of ambulance personnel over the years. I returned from the hospital after the formalities and we had our Christmas dinner. It was surreal, paper hats, crackers, trying to explain to my mother and to our children what had happened when in truth we couldn't grasp it ourselves. Then a blur of family, of memories, of tears and regrets; we should have told this gentle nice man how much he had meant to us all and suddenly he was gone and it was too late.

Our Sara was just a little one when her grandfather died and he had been very fond of her. She left just as suddenly and it is our hope that they are together. These are sad memories at Christmas, but you just can't have the happy reflections and ignore the rest of life. What we can do is remember the good times and the real people and the happiness of times past.

I think of my father of course particularly at this time of year and of the good times we had. His reluctance to leave the river bank while there was the remotest chance that another trout might be caught was legendary. I remember his unchristian satisfaction at the death of a doctor who some 20 years before had told him that he only had a year to live. This story was worn out by repetition to medical friends and family.

You were a lifestyle nightmare Dad. You were overweight, had high blood pressure and ate all the wrong things. You worried more than anybody I ever knew about any matter, however trivial. Yet you made it to 84 without serious illness. I hope I carry your genes and I hope I am half the man you were.

December 29th, 2009

Turning back the clock to meet a patient

Out of the blue, Mr and Mrs David Doyle of Enniscorthy invited the HA and I to the wedding of their daughter Jeanne to Mr Aidan Kinane. A long time ago I operated upon Jeanne in Our Lady's Hospital for Sick Children in Crumlin. Following surgery and initial follow-up, I told her mother and grandmother that I would not need to see her again until her wedding day. Jeanne, who is now a teacher in Rockwell College, told me she was marrying a fine Tipperary man. I want you Jeanne and your family to know that your invitation was very special to me and is deeply appreciated. I wish you and Aidan every happiness, in every way. To digress slightly I wish your charges in Rockwell and the college itself success in the future. I appreciate that you might have other things on your mind.

Jeanne was referred to me for surgery by Prof Conor Ward who held the chair of paediatrics at UCD and was a cardiologist of note on the world stage. Conor described, in the Journal of the Irish Medical Association in 1964, a hitherto unobserved familial cardiac rhythm disorder in children. The following year, a Dr C Romano independently noted the same arrhythmia and published his findings in the Lancet. The complex is known as the Ward-Romano syndrome and is one of the causes of sudden death in childhood and adolescence. Now when noted, it can be treated. Conor was largely responsible for my appointment in Crumlin and became a great colleague and friend.

At the beginning of the unit in Crumlin, great strides were being made in this facet of heart surgery. This was largely due to a greater understanding of the anatomy of congenital heart disease, much of this facilitated by the retention and study of postmortem hearts. This showed the complexities of anatomical variation and was absolutely necessary to allow the surgeons devise operations to remedy them. This led to problems down the line, not foreseen in those pioneering days. The operations were only one aspect of the treatment. The anaesthesiology and the intensive care had to be of very high standard and they progressed very rapidly with skilled and enthusiastic staff to a stage where today they are second to none.

It is deeply distressing to hear of theatre and intensive care closures and staff shortages in this wonderful unit delivering world-class treatment. It is but another example of the havoc wreaked in our health service by this woeful regime. Let nobody tell me that our health service is improving.

In the earliest days when Conor and I and Dr Brian Denham provided the service, we needed to develop the nursing intensive care team. Sr Augustine (Gussie) from Crumlin and Conor's wife Pauline uprooted themselves from Dublin to undertake the paediatric intensive care course in London's Great Ormond Street Children's Hospital. Thousands of children benefited from that little seed and more will benefit still if the little patients who need help are not blighted by the little people who exercise power without understanding or compassion. On retirement Conor and Pauline went to live in London where some of their family were working. Conor immediately became involved in major voluntary work for children with Down syndrome. He is that kind of man and my life has been immeasurably richer for knowing himself and Pauline.

There is a bit of "white horse syndrome" about meeting former patients. They all remember you because their cardiac surgery was such a major event in their lives. For you it was your day's work. You knew some through other fields and some you remembered vividly because they had helped your hair turn grey. Large numbers became involved in support groups and fundraising to ensure better facilities for those needing surgery in the future.

On another occasion, in a shop in the west the local fisheries inspector said: "Look after the surgeon Jim, he saved my son's life." "Well and if he did," says your man, "my brother wasn't so lucky." Well you can't and didn't win them all. You could only do your best. However, trying to function without adequate facilities poses ethical and moral questions that are unanswerable.

April 13th, 2010

The stark choices that can mean life or death

*And for these ends, to practise tolerance
and live together with one another in
peace and as good neighbours*

These inspirational words come from the United Nations Charter of 1945. A brief glance around you shows that we're not quite there yet. It should be an easy concept to grasp and subscribe to, but it's not. I am not entering philosophical debate here; one man's tolerance constitutes an abomination for another. Most want to live in an evolving and progressive society with norms that the vast majority accept. Sometimes, this comfortably woolly concept assumes a hard shape and pins you to the wall, requiring decisions that you would rather not be forced to make.

During my surgical sojourn in England, my chief, Leon Abrams, had a large practice among Jehovah's Witnesses. In those days, a lot of blood was used in open heart surgery. It was used to prime the capacity of the machine itself, and all the tubing connecting to the patient's vessels. Blood was replaced as it was lost during surgery, and was given freely post operatively.

Nowadays, blood is used sparingly if at all, but is available if required. This is so in emergency cases and in trauma, as recently witnessed in the case of the young Irish footballer with the ruptured hepatic artery, dealt with so capably by my old friend and colleague, Gerry McEntee, in the Mater. There are many other surgical and obstetrical emergencies that require blood urgently. We have an excellent blood transfusion service in Ireland, serving the patients who need our unstinting donations.

One morning, faced with a difficult re-operation in a Jehovah's Witness, the team discussed the problem with Abe. It quickly came down to the bottom line. Would he let the patient die, knowing that blood transfusion might well save them? Abe, as he was known, looked thoughtfully at us all. By chance the team on that day comprised Jewish, Catholic and Muslim surgeons. "Gentlemen," he said, "we are all members of minority religions here in Britain; we must all respect and tolerate each other's beliefs." I am not sure how much we all agreed with his stance and, indeed, how it stood with our medical ethic, *Primum non nocere* or "First, do no harm", but in time I was to find out. Some of the patients became very pale after their surgery, but in my time with him, Abe never lost such a patient.

On my return to a consultant post in Ireland, I was asked to undertake surgery on a number of such patients. It was my turn to take responsibility and be other than a spear holder in the group photograph. I had to explain to the patient and their family that their faith placed them in greater jeopardy than similar patients who did not share their beliefs. They always explained their stance to me and quoted the biblical references upon which it was based. I told them that as a doctor I respected their beliefs and would do my very best for them. It made life more difficult, but that was a consequence of agreeing to undertake the operation in the first place. In practice, I never had to face the unspoken stark choice in this moral and ethical minefield. Adults have the right to exercise such choice we are told, but do they – and is it absolute? Would I have let the mother of three young children die?

Would I have let a child die because of the parent's beliefs? I never found out, but the problem remains for surgeons who have to face up to such challenges and make a judgment that is personal and cannot be delegated to committee. It's your call and, as Edmund Burke wrote, "Your representative owes you, not his industry only, but his judgment; and he betrays, instead of serving you, if he sacrifices it to your opinion."

Burke was referring to politicians and, indeed, it should apply to all public representatives. It applies equally to doctors. Medicine is not best practised by committee. Somebody has to make the decision regarding treatment, explain it and stand by it. "Doctor knows best" is regarded as paternalistic in these sophisticated times. If you feel, as is your right, that committee knows best, then good luck to you. There is no universal decision that will be right all the time. If patients approach their doctor with suspicion or distrust, the results may well be bad for both.

June 1st, 2010